OP

HUMAN NATURE

IN THE LIGHT OF PSYCHOPATHOLOGY

HUMAN NATURE

IN THE LIGHT OF PSYCHOPATHOLOGY

BY

KURT GOLDSTEIN

SCHOCKEN BOOKS · NEW YORK

CONTENTS

CONTENTS

FOREWORD — 1963

When Schocken Books kindly offered to reissue the William James Lectures, "Human Nature in the Light of Psychopathology," delivered at Harvard in 1940, I naturally wondered whether I should not add the results of my later research. I decided that it would neither be necessary nor appropriate to do so. To burden the book with further detail would merely divert the reader's attention from the central conceptions. It would also detract from the original format of a series of lectures, a presentation which is particularly appropriate for my ideas.

Presenting the material as individual lectures, each concerned with a special characteristic, may be misleading insofar as it could suggest that we are dealing with separate parts of human nature. The reader may be spared this inference if he grasps the nature of the holistic method (which I have described in detail in *The Organism*). From this point of view, any phenomenon can be understood only when considered in relation to every other phenomenon; it can be evaluated only by recognizing its significance in the functioning of the organism as a whole. The lectures are arranged in a definite sequence, thus the reader will proceed to grasp my concept of man just as I myself developed it in the course of investigating different characteristics of human nature.

While I have not basically changed my conception of "human nature" since these lectures, I think something should be said about certain new observations. These concern the relationship between the abstract and concrete attitudes, which plays an essential role in my concept of man. I had assumed that these two attitudes function interdependently. Concrete behavior appears concomitantly with abstract, very often it depends upon the latter, is even initiated by it. Therefore, we are surprised to observe an individual who seems able to exist on the concrete level alone — for example, the human infant. He comes into the world as a very limited organism, particularly since his abstract capacity is not yet developed. He escapes the threat of death because certain inborn mechanisms immediately come into action; but even they can only work if the infant is protected by the people around him, especially his mother. This protection consists of building up an environment with which the infant can come to terms. It presupposes insight into the physiological and psychological needs and the maturational changes of the infantile organism. This insight, and the tendency to act accordingly in the interest of the infant, results from the mother's using her abstract capacity. Thus, the factors determining whether or not the infant survives are distributed between two persons — the infant and the mother.

This dependence of the concrete behavior of one person on the abstract capacity of another achieves general significance when we realize that it also occurs in an adult under special conditions, as when confronted with a task for which he does not *need* to apply the abstract attitude — in fact, were he to use it, it might even disturb the fulfillment of the task. This, for instance, is the case when an industrial worker has to continually perform the same operation — a motor automatism. But his concrete behavior is made possible only because the machinery he uses was constructed through the abstract capacity of another. I cannot discuss here why a human being with the capacity for abstraction is willing to work in such an automatic way, but this serious problem concerns not only the industrial worker but to a greater or lesser degree the behavior of all of us in civilized society.

Such non-use of indivdual capacities, due to the demands of the culture, helps us understand the much-discussed behavior of "primitive people." These people appeared to behave so concretely that one felt justified in assuming that they had an inborn inferior mentality, which was termed the "pre-logical mind." New anthropological research has revealed that this assumption is wrong. Their daily life (like much of our own) is so organized that most of their tasks are adequately fulfilled without the use of abstraction. The late anthropologist Paul Radin distinguished between two types of people: "non-thinkers," who live strictly in accordance with the rules of society, and "thinkers." While the number of thinkers may be small, they play a major role in the tribe; they are the people who formulate concepts and organize them in systems, which are then taken over—generally without criticism — by the non-thinkers. Yet, because the thinkers are so closely connected with community life, they also participate, more or less, in the non-rational activities of the group. This may give the erroneous impression that their mentality too is "primitive."

Thus, when we distinguish the non-use of abstraction from the absence of abstraction, we need no longer assume mental inferiority among "primitive" peoples. This is important, for we must recognize that members of "primitive" societies can play a role in the United Nations, participating in decisions of the greatest significance to the whole world. Since I cannot here discuss primitive societies at length, I refer the reader to the work of Paul Radin, and my paper, "Concerning the Concept of Primitivity," in *Culture and History,* Essays in Honor of Paul Radin, Columbia University Press, 1960.

All adequate human behavior presupposes concrete performance and abstract attitude. While an action is always performed by the person himself in a concrete way, the influence of the abstract attitude behind it can originate either in the same person or in another. But human life cannot be wholly understood through these attitudes alone. To grasp the fullness of life, one must consider another area of human experience. I have called this the "sphere of immediacy." While concrete-abstract behavior guarantees order and security, the sphere of immediacy makes unity possible between the world and ourselves, particularly in our relationship to other human beings.

It is not easy to describe this sphere. To enter it, we must try to disregard somewhat the "natural science" attitude which, since it does not comprise the totality of human nature, appears "unnatural" in this sphere. We achieve this immediacy only by surrendering ourselves to the world with which we come in contact. When we do this, the words we use to describe our experiences may appear strange and reminiscent of the language of poets. Such words reveal a new world not normally observed in our practical or scientific behavior. More properly, we intentionally repress this world because its influence may disturb the stability and security of the subject-object world of our culture. Yet these experiences of immediacy are related to the same world in which we otherwise live. They represent its deepest character. We are here involved in our totality, while in the subject-object world we experience only isolated parts of ourselves and the world — a point of view which may be preferable for special purposes.

In my book *The Organism* (re-issued by Beacon Press, 1963) I discuss the importance of adequate order between us and the world for the attainment of true knowledge. I must stress here that the impulse to *seek* for knowledge originates fundamentally in the sphere of immediacy. Through it, human life acquires its dynamic character. In this sphere is not only the source of all creativity, the development of friendship, love and religion, but also those possibilities for failure, sorrow and anxiety which are part of our life. While being in the sphere of immediacy may involve danger, we deliberately take this risk, since only thus can we realize ourselves fully (see my paper "On Emotions," *J. Psychol.*, 1951, *31*, p. 37).

The sphere of immediacy is already present in the first year of life (see my paper "The Smiling of the Infant and the Problem of Understanding the Other," *J. Psychol.*, 1957, *44*, p. 175). Within it the adequate relationship between mother and infant originates. Later it is especially significant for our understanding of what goes on in the "other." How deeply our life is rooted in the sphere of immediacy is shown by our reaction to any discrepancy between it and the subject-object sphere, which disturbs their unity or, more accurately, their harmony. If, for instance, on meeting a beloved friend we smilingly approach him in expectation of happiness and are deceived in this expectation, we may not simply have a sense of error, i.e., a failure in the concrete-abstract sphere; rather, we feel the ensuing shock as something dangerous which touches the core of our nature. Our well-being and possibilities for self-realization are endangered, our very existence and that of the world.

For they are all based upon the experience of real unity with the other; they are experiences in the sphere of immediacy.

Finally, I would like to make a remark about the methodological procedure behind my characterizations of human nature. All my progress has been based on the study of concrete phenomena and, before drawing any conclusions, on giving myself a clear account of what I am doing. Furthermore, by applying the holistic method I have not only felt I was on the right path, but also gained the courage to characterize biological knowledge more specifically. I recognized that the organism's procedure for finding that adequacy between itself and the world which guarantees its existence is essentially similar to our procedure for finding the concept of the living being. It is this similarity which makes biological knowledge possible. Biological knowledge appears, therefore, as a form of biological being. My concept of human nature corresponds to the specific form of biological being which presents itself in man. We only can fully "understand" — in contrast to "know about" — those forms of existence which are basically like us.

KURT GOLDSTEIN

New York 1963.

HUMAN NATURE

IN THE LIGHT OF PSYCHOPATHOLOGY

I

THE HOLISTIC APPROACH AND THE ANALYTIC METHOD IN SCIENCE

PERHAPS the most distinctive feature of the nineteenth century is the amazing increase during that period of detailed scientific knowledge in various fields, acquired through an admirable use of what we may call the "atomistic" method.* The accumulation of so many thousands of facts brought an immense enrichment and refinement into the organization of the world, and in many ways made life easier, but it was followed by appalling complications in human existence. Along with the immense specialization of the sciences there occurred a marked disintegration of the life of the individual. Increasing rationalization and systematization produced a chaotic state which forced the human being into an existence that became more and more unsuited to his nature. The high development of science and technology was, of course, only the expression of a certain stage of cultural and economic development, but it was a very characteristic expression and in its turn

---

* This term is intended to designate any method which uses a dissecting procedure and tries to derive laws from the parts studied. The term "atomistic" will be used interchangeably with "analytic" and "dissecting."

exerted a strong influence on cultural and economic conditions.

Among those who early recognized the fatal consequences of the scientific approach to human living was William James, and his entire thinking was directed toward finding a more satisfactory basis for the conduct of life. Throughout his philosophical work the question of the relation between life and knowledge was fundamental. Concerning the answer, he had no doubt. Knowledge for him had meaning only if a better practical life could be based upon it. That he considered mind as something that has use and that can be defined only from this point of view is very characteristic of his approach to thinking.

From such a point of view, he analyzed the process of knowledge and came to stress the importance of "belief," in addition to scientific reasoning, as a special source from which truth may arise. As Ralph Barton Perry has clearly shown in his book, *In the Spirit of William James* (New Haven, 1938), James realized that scientific knowledge is based ultimately on some creed, a creed which is the more significant because it eventually provides the basis upon which all action can be predicated. And the rationale of practical action was, for James, the final goal of knowledge.

This is not the place to evaluate the conclusions James drew from his appraisal of belief. We certainly cannot follow him in all his inferences — as, for example, when he was induced to give a special account of the phenomena of what is called psychic research. We must pay homage, however, to the fact that he tried both to set knowledge free and to free human existence from the strait-jacket of merely analyzing, anatomizing, and rationalizing, by which science and life were governed in his time. He threw into relief the holistic point of view from which alone he found human life understandable, and thus disclosed the whole complexity of concrete human existence. In this respect he stands in line with philosophers like Dilthey, Bergson, Whitehead, and Dewey. In his aim of concreteness, and in his emphasis on the holistic point of view, he was a forerunner of the *Gestalt* psychologists, of such biologists as Child, Coghill, Herrick, and Lashley, of psychiatrists like Adolf Meyer and Trigant Burrow, and finally of that approach through which I myself have attempted to treat medicine, psychology, and biology.[1]

To the physician, the need for emphasis upon the practical is clearly evident. Even in his theoretical considerations, it is natural for him to be drawn in a practical direction, because the problem of healing is the very heart of his activity. In the approach toward healing today we are no longer preoccupied with the innumerable single phenomena in disease; we know that these phenomena are not the essentials of the disease. More and more we approach the conviction that the essential element of disease is the shock to the existence of the individual caused by the disturbance of the well-regulated functioning of the organism by disease. If restoration is out of the question, the only goal of the physician is to provide the patient with the possibility of existing in spite of his defect.[2] To do this one has to consider each single symptom in terms of its functional significance for the total personality of the patient. Thus it is obviously necessary for the physician to know the *organism as a whole*, the total personality of his patient, and the change which this organism as a whole has suffered through disease. The whole organism, the individual human being, becomes the center of interest.

Naturally one cannot fail to observe that a true insight into the condition of the individual is to be gained only if the individual is considered as part of the whole of nature, particularly of the human society to which it belongs. Many manifestations of disease can be understood only in the light of their social origin and can be eliminated only by considering this origin. Such a view leads to the study of the interrelationships between the individual and society, the differences between nations and races, and the variations in individuals themselves.

All these questions have brought the problem of the nature of man to the fore. Since the end of the last century this problem has gained more and more in general interest. Following a period of relative security during the second half of the last century, the world situation became fraught with increasing uncertainty. Ultimately the foundations of human existence were doubted or shattered altogether. This state of affairs prompted the question: May not this disaster have been produced through a false idea of the nature of human beings? Did the institutions and organizations of society crumble because they failed to fit the capacities of that nature, and were men therefore unable to sustain them? In the western world these institutions were based especially upon a high estimate of the human capacity called reason, which since the time of the Greeks had been considered as the most important and the most fundamental capacity of the human race. Could this assumption possibly have been wrong? *Is* man a being governed mainly by reason? Or is it incorrect to suppose that it is this capacity which principally separates man from animals? Ought not the human being perhaps to be considered only as a species of animal, possibly uniquely developed, but an animal just the same, motivated in his activities by "instincts" and "drives" and not by reason and free will?

The experiences of the last few decades, in Europe in particular, have awakened great doubt regarding the character of human nature. Qualities have been proclaimed from the housetops as the highest virtues which in their very nature stand in complete opposition to those social and moral ideas which have formed the basis of western culture for thousands of years. The success of these new ideas has shaken the old faith. The nature of man has thus become problematic at its very core, and this is likely to affect the whole existence of the human race. Thus it is understandable that, as the German philosopher Max Scheler [3] said, "in the ten thousand years of human history ours is the first era in which man has become a problem to himself, in which he no longer knows what he is, and at the same time knows that he does not know it."

Based on this situation, the increased interest of scientists in man has emerged in various realms — in anthropology and ethnology, which have tried to gain a better insight into the nature of man in general, especially through a comparison of "civilized" and "primitive" peoples; in medicine and psychology,[4] where a science of the individual personality has been more and more urgently demanded; and finally in philosophy.

It was natural that, in the development of this approach to man in his entirety, interest in the single phenomenon, which till then science had stressed in all its various fields, should have diminished. This meant a turning away from the atomistic and mechanistic approach, from a mere theoretical attitude, toward empiricism and concreteness. This tendency was to be observed in the procedure in the individual departments of science as well as in the increasing concern with synthesizing the results of the diverse sciences which are concerned with the nature of man.

Thus anthropology, which used to take into consideration little but physical phenomena, now tries to base its conclusions not only upon the results of physical anthropology but also upon those of ethnology, psychology, sociology, philosophy, and pathology. That this elimination of the lines of demarcation between the various sciences in order to attain a clearer view of the real facts — a characteristic of the modern approach of biological science, especially of the science of man — was familiar to James may be judged from such statements as: "There is no valid demarcation between philosophy and physiological psychology."

When a student of human nature bases his studies on the results of one special science, he has nothing but a starting point; he will never derive a correct answer to his questions from the material of a single realm alone. In this connection, I should like to consider my own use of pathological material.

With our holistic approach to human nature, we are faced with a very difficult epistemological problem. For us there is no doubt that the atomistic method is the only legitimate scientific procedure for gaining facts. Knowledge of human nature has to be based on phenomena disclosed in this way. But is it possible to proceed from material gained by the use of this method to a science of the organism as a whole, to a science of the nature of man? [5]

If the organism were a sum of parts which we could study separately, there would be no difficulty in combining our knowledge about the parts to form a science of the whole. But all attempts to understand the organism as a whole directly from these phenomena have met with very little success. They have not been successful, we may conclude, because the organism is not such a sum of parts. The analytic experiment may not be suitable in principle for finding out the real constituent attributes of an organism and leading to a recognition of the organism as a whole.

If the organism is a whole and each section of it functions normally within that whole, then in the analytic experiment, which isolates the sections as it studies them, the properties and functions of any part must be modified by their isolation from the whole of the organism. Thus they cannot reveal the function of these parts in normal life. There are innumerable facts which demonstrate how the functioning of a field is changed by its isolation. If we want to use the results of such experiments for understanding the activity of the organism in normal life (that is, as a whole), we must know in what way the condition of isolation modifies the functioning, and we must take these modifications into account. We have every reason to occupy ourselves very carefully with this condition of isolation; as we shall see later, many a phenomenon of human life is understandable only in terms of the effects of isolation.

In order to understand these modifications of functions in isolation we must discuss the function of the nervous system.[6] Such an excursion will also be valuable for the understanding of certain other problems which we shall have to discuss later. Naturally, I must confine myself to the most important facts, and can only outline them in apodeictic form.

The organism, we assume, is a unit. We shall consider the functioning of this unit by means of the facts gained through studies of the nervous system, because the functioning of this system lends itself especially well to explanation. The nervous system is an apparatus which always functions as a whole. It is always in a state of excitation, never at rest. All performances are expressions of changes in this condition of perpetual activity, which are caused by the stimuli that impinge upon the organism. These changes always concern the entire system, but not in the same manner throughout, the special effect of any stimulus becoming apparent in one particular place. Stimulation of the eyes by light is usually followed by movements of the pupils or of other eye muscles, and by vision. If we assume that stimulation spreads over the whole system, this localized effect can be explained in the following way. Stimulation may change the excitation in the whole system, but it changes it in an effective way particularly in the part of the body near the entrance of the stimulus. We call this the local or *spatial near effect*. The particular effect of a stimulus, however, results not only from the special excitation of those parts of the body which are in the neighborhood of the point of entrance of the stimulus, but also from the specific receptiveness of definite parts of the nervous system to specific stimuli. The eyes, for example, are specifically adapted to be affected by light, the nose by odor, and so on. We call this the *functional near effect*, in distinction to the spatial near effect. The performance caused by a stimulus is the expression of the excitation of both the spatial and the functional near effect. The processes set off by the stimulus are not restricted to a part of the nervous system the excitation of which corresponds to the performance — for example, the perception of an object; the rest of the nervous system is also more or less involved, and there is a characteristic relationship between the excitation in the near part and excitation arising in the distant parts. We speak in this connection of the near effect as the *figure* process and of the excitation in the rest of the nervous system as the *ground* process. In the same way we speak of *figure* and *background* in a performance. Any excitation in the nervous system has the character of a figure-ground process. Any performance invariably shows this figure-ground character.

When you look at a picture you see and understand at once what is figure and what background. The terms "figure" and "ground" have, indeed, been borrowed from our visual experience. However, they fit not only visual configurations but all other configurations as well. For example, if you raise your arm vertically, the exact execution of this movement requires, as you can feel in yourself and observe in others, a quite definite position of the rest of the body. The raised arm is the figure; the rest of the body is the background. Figure and background can be discriminated as readily in speaking, thinking, feeling, etc. A word, for instance, is understandable only within a definite context, within a definite sentence, within a certain cultural sphere.

Habitually we ignore the background of a performance and pay attention only to the figure. From the standpoint of systematic observation and methodology this is false, for figure and background are intimately interconnected. Neither can be properly evaluated without the other.

As an example of the influence of the background on the figure let me recall first how the impression of a simple color changes if it is presented on different backgrounds. Just so, the execution of any precise movement of a limb demands a definite attitude of the rest of the body. The most superficial glance at the way we walk will show that the correct movements of our legs in walking depend upon definite movements of our arms and head. When for any reason freedom of arms and head is impeded, the gait changes immediately; in short, when the background changes, the figure (the performance) also changes.

In the normal organism a definite stimulus produces under the same conditions approximately the same figure and ground configuration, and with it approximately the same reaction. For example, a

person always has about the same visual acuity;
that is, the same visual stimulus — a point of definite
extension and color on a definite background — produces the same visual experience. The reaction is
based on what is called the threshold of vision. If
the threshold did not remain approximately equal
under normal conditions, it would not be possible
for a given object or part of the physical world to
arouse the same experience again and again nor
should we be able to react to the same situation
in a consistent way. Only through such uniformity
is an ordered life possible. Otherwise our world
would change constantly, and we ourselves should
change, too. But this is not the case. Our world
remains relatively constant despite all the changes
in it, and we, too, remain about the same.

On the other hand, there is no doubt that each
stimulus produces a change in the substratum which
changes its excitability, with the result that a new
stimulus — equal to the former one — gives rise to
an effect different from the previous one.[7] Now how
is it possible that in spite of this change of excitability through stimulation the threshold remains
approximately the same, that the organism remains
about the same, and that it reacts in about the same
way to a later stimulus? This constancy is achieved
only by virtue of the fact that in normal life excitation which has been changed by a stimulus returns, after a period of time, to its former state; that
is, if no new stimulation occurs, it returns to a state of

equilibrium. The presupposition of constancy is that the change in excitability caused by the stimulus is only temporary.

This equalization process fixes the threshold and, with this, creates constancy, ordered behavior, and secures the very existence of the organism. Normal equalization demands the working of the whole organism; it is, in fact, an equalization between the excitation in near and distant parts. Normal life is ordered life because the equalization process takes place in relation to the tasks of the whole organism. This is not the case under experimental and pathological conditions. In an experiment we deliberately isolate the parts we wish to study. This is perfectly evident in experiments on animals where, for example, we separate the spinal cord from the brain and study the functioning of the isolated spinal cord by stimulating it when it is cut off from the rest of the nervous system. But there is no difference in principle in our method of studying reflexes in human beings, or elementary functions such as vision, hearing, etc. Here, so to speak, we functionally isolate the part to be tested, excluding by special arrangements the co-working of the rest of the organism. Pathological processes, too, are rather like the experiments on animals in the way they isolate parts of the nervous system. Pathology consists in the destruction of some regions of the nervous system, as a result of which the latter is divided into parts, each of which functions in isolation from the rest. This separation may take place in various parts of the nervous system, and the symptoms in different fields correspond to the isolation of different parts.

Now how does isolation change the functioning of the nervous system and modify its reactions? [8] We shall mention here only such facts as are important for the explanation to follow.

1. The reactions to stimuli in an isolated part are *abnormally strong*. For example, knee jerks in an animal with a lesion of the upper part of the spinal cord are exaggerated. The explanation is that the excitation produced by the stimulus, which normally spreads over the whole nervous system, is now restricted to a smaller part of the organ and therefore has a greater effect.

2. The reactions are of *abnormal duration*, because the normal equalization process is disturbed.

3. The reactions are bound to the stimulus in an abnormal way. We call this phenomenon *abnormal stimulus bondage*, or *forced responsiveness to stimuli*. Normally a reaction is determined not only by the stimulus but also by the after-effects of former reactions, which are elicited by the stimulus at the same time. These after-effects correspond to processes not only in the stimulated part of the organism but also in the rest of the organism. Now if the stimulated part is more or less detached from the rest of the organism, those processes cannot be utilized in the reaction as they normally would. In consequence, the outside stimuli gain an abnormal

predominance and compel the organism to react in a more than normal way. This effect of isolation is to be seen particularly clearly in sick people. They are in general much more under the influence of external stimuli, less capable of freeing themselves from a stimulus which has touched them, than well people.

This abnormal bondage to an existing stimulus appears also when the stimulation originates not externally but in an excitation of any part within the organism, if this part is isolated from the rest of the organism. Thus *isolated processes within the organism may determine the reactions of the sick individual in an abnormal, compulsive way.* In the mental field this finds its expression in the abnormal predominance of particular thoughts, ideas, or compulsive activities. To the individual himself these phenomena seem strange and not a part of him.

4. A further change of the form of the reaction in an isolated part is the appearance of abnormal rigidity on the one hand and alternating reactions to a single stimulus on the other. This is the consequence of a disturbance of the normal figure-ground process. If the stimulus which touches an isolated part is adequate for the activity of this part, the reaction, the "figure," becomes abnormally fixed because of the lack of the equalization process.* If the stimulus is adequate only to a section of this part, then a reaction may appear which corresponds

* Cf. point 2, above.

to that section. But this excitation, the "figure," has no constancy, because the rest of the isolated part does not represent an adequate background. Excitation of this part may gain preponderance after a certain time, and a phenomenon appears that corresponds to the stimulation of the rest of the part. After a time this reaction, which is also not a "good" figure and therefore has no stability, disappears, and a reaction corresponding to the excitation of the first stimulated section returns, and so on, in alternation. This we call "lability." Such alternating reactions are frequently observed in patients with mental diseases.

5. The detachment of a part of the organism from the rest more or less deprives the activities of that part of content. Therefore actions in isolation are simpler or, as we say, more "primitive."

Isolation phenomena are characteristic of pathological conditions. They may also occur in normal life if stimulation gains an abnormal strength or an abnormal duration which hinders the normal equalization process. We shall see later that much of the behavior of normal people becomes understandable when considered as phenomena in an isolation caused through abnormal outer-world conditions.

I should like to illustrate the effect of isolation by some simple examples, from experiences open to everybody. We can isolate processes in our own bodies by special experimental procedure. We can expose our visual apparatus to abnormal stimula-

tion, as in after-image experiments, where we allow
a color to act intensively on our eyes. In that case
we obtain both an abnormal after-effect and repeated
alternations of opposite (complementary) color sen-
sations. Or take a similar phenomenon in the motor
field. If, with the arm hanging loosely, one presses
the hand against a wall so that the deltoid muscle is
strongly innervated, the arm rises by itself. The less
attention the subject pays to the arm, thereby isolating it, the more striking the phenomenon is. If
one succeeds in this isolation, one experiences an
alternating movement, the arm rising and falling
several times. The Danish psychologist, Rubin, -to
whom we are greatly indebted for the elucidation of
the figure-ground problem, has constructed a figure
which is designed especially for the demonstration
of the alternation phenomenon (Fig. 1).[9] When we
look at it passively, oscillation appears very readily;
we see now a white vase on a black background, now
two black faces on a white background. We also
feel that this oscillation is, so to speak, detached
from our personality, that it takes place almost
against our will.

All these phenomena are "isolated" from us. The
isolation becomes particularly clear if we succeed
in bringing one of the phenomena into closer relationship to ourselves. Then the character of lability
disappears, or at least decreases strongly. Some
events gain definiteness and stability. That is to be
observed especially in the last example. When we do

not take the figure merely as a visual picture, but
look at the vase or the two faces as if they were real
objects, the lability lessens. Apparently the experience of alternation corresponds to a more passive

Fig. 1

stimulation of a part of the organism, namely, the
visual apparatus — that is, to the stimulation of a
part which, functionally, is relatively isolated from
the whole personality. The more complete the approach of the whole organism to an object in the
outer world, the more constant the object. Because
in everyday life we usually make the complete approach, the objects of the outer world are definitely
figures, and there is never under normal conditions

a change of figure and ground or even an uncertainty about what is figure and what is ground.

There is no doubt that, if we take into consideration the changes that occur through isolation, the phenomena revealed by the isolating method can be used in a way adapted to our purpose, which is to understand the organism as a whole. Even then we do not know whether the phenomena we observe correspond to the essential properties of the organism or whether they may represent merely accidental expressions of the organism under certain — possibly very unnatural — conditions. As we shall see later, we shall come nearer to our goal by using another methodological procedure.* This consists in the use of observations under certain conditions which we call preferred conditions. The phenomena observed under these conditions — we call them preferred behavior or preferred performances — will bring us somewhat nearer to the true constituents of the organism. Even then, however, we remain still within the realm of the analytic method, and we can never be sure that we possess the attributes characteristic of the organism as a whole. Thus our endeavor to gain any knowledge of the nature of man seems to be doomed to failure. Certainly there is no possibility of achieving biological knowledge on the sole basis of phenomena which can be determined by the analytic method. In making this statement, however, I do not wish to arouse the impression that we

* See p. 174.

underrate the significance of such phenomena or that we believe there is no real possibility of gaining biological knowledge. Concerning the first point, I may say that we do not accept these phenomena as undistorted manifestations of the nature of the organism. They must first prove their "significance" for the organism. They are the material with which we have to deal, but the value they have for our understanding of the behavior of an organism depends upon our conception of the latter. In this way they lose their apparent character of self-evident facts. Thus what biology in general believes to be the basis of its body of knowledge, the "facts," becomes most problematic. For this reason many facts in the history of science have proved to be without value for the advancement of our knowledge. I believe that this skepticism toward what we call facts is a basic requirement for fruitful work in all branches of natural science. It is only this skepticism which eliminates existing biases by preparing the ground for posing the fundamental question: Which phenomena are biologically relevant, and which not? Which phenomena are biological "facts," and which not?

A criterion for that relevancy can be offered only by a conception of the organism in its qualitative organization and holistic functioning. This conception is the basis of biological knowledge. How can we gain it? It is not a mere synthesis of separate phenomena. It is true that the latter point to the organization in question, but such a picture of the organism cannot be obtained *directly* from them. Neither can it be obtained by means of the simple inductive method. It is not a question of generalizing or of applying to other circumstances the results of previous observations, and thus of enlarging our knowledge progressively by induction. This factor certainly plays a large part in concrete scientific work, but it does not furnish us with knowledge, nor does it make a scientific description of biological phenomena possible. Yet neither is the process of acquiring biological knowledge a deductive procedure. We do not adhere in any way to the a priori method of preconceived categories applied to the nature of life, to the differences between animals and "human beings," etc.

We do not try to construct the architecture of the organism by a mere addition of brick to brick; rather we try to discover the actual *Gestalt* of the intrinsic structure of this building, a *Gestalt* through which some phenomena may become intelligible as belonging to a unitary, ordered, relatively constant formation of a specific structure, and other phenomena may become intelligible as not belonging to it. The picture of the organism must be of such a kind that it allows us to differentiate among the observed phenomena between the members which really belong to it and phenomena corresponding to less relevant arbitrary connections between contingent parts.

The concept which should help us to make this

differentiation is grounded in the reality which constitutes being, but it is an idea, a criterion by which something is known (*Erkenntnisgrund*). We can arrive at it only by using a special procedure of cognition — a form of creative activity by which we build a picture of the organism on the basis of the facts gained through the analytic method, in a form of ideation similar to the procedure of an artist. It is a sort of ideation, however, which springs ever and again from empirical facts, and never fails to be grounded in and substantiated by them. Biological knowledge is the result of the continued extension of our experience. The German poet, Goethe, to whom we owe much for important discoveries in the field of biology, has called this procedure of acquiring knowledge *Schau*, and the "picture" by which the individual phenomenon becomes understandable (as a modification), the *Urbild* (prototype). To recommend such a type of cognitive procedure may suggest that we are headed for metaphysical or even mystical fields. This impression can readily be dispelled by pointing to such a trivial biological phenomenon as the acquisition of any skill — bicycling, for example. We execute inappropriate bodily movements — that is, movements which are determined by partitive aspects and which are only partially relevant for correct bicycle-riding — until suddenly we are capable of maintaining our balance and of moving in the correct way. All these initial exercises are only indirectly related to the performance finally achieved.

They are not aimless, of course, but merely incorrect movements which in themselves never lead directly to the correct movements. They are necessary because the correct performance can be reached only by continuous modifications of those movements. The correct movements appear suddenly, however, when a state is reached in which the procedure of the organism is adequate to the environmental conditions. This adequacy is *experienced* by us. The procedure in this situation also includes insight into the correct procedure in bicycling. We continually try to bring about this experience of adequacy, and the correct procedure, until it becomes the performance that we set going when we attempt to ride a bicycle.

In essence the biological knowledge we are seeking is akin to this phenomenon in which the capacity of the organism becomes adequate to environmental conditions. This is the fundamental biological process by virtue of which the actualization of the organism, and with that its existence, is made possible. Whenever we speak of the nature of the organism, of the idea, the picture, or the concept of the organism, we have in mind the essentials for the occurrence of an adequate relationship between the organism and its environment. From these, in principle, that picture arises which we have to grasp in determining the nature of man. In doing so we are subjected to practically the same difficulties of procedure as the organism in learning: we are obliged to discover what the relationship is between concept and reality.

In practice the difficulties which this method may seem to entail are not so great as they appear in theoretical consideration. In practice we usually venture to pass from the plane of partitive facts (which corresponds to the isolating method) to this other form of cognition. The more conscious we are of the theoretical justification of this procedure and of its consequences, the less concerned we need be about doing so. We usually proceed in such a way that from certain facts gained by analysis we sketch a picture of the whole organism, which in turn, so long as we encounter discrepancies between this picture and factual experience, stimulates further questions and investigations. Upon the basis of new inquiries the picture of the whole is again modified, and the process of discovering new discrepancies and making new inquiries follows, and so on. By such empirical procedure in a dialectic manner, a progressively more adequate knowledge of the nature of the organism, of its "essence" (*Wesen*), is acquired, and an increasingly correct evaluation of the observed facts, and of whether or not they are essential to the organism, is obtained.

The process of acquiring knowledge which we have described as characteristic of biology does not differ in principle from that used in other sciences. As skepticism toward a naïve copy-theory of knowledge grew, and as it was realized that "empirical" facts are not a simple expression of reality but are also produced through the method of investigation, it became more and more clear that it was the task of natural science to transcend "empirical" facts and create images, "symbols," which are suited for gaining a coherent understanding of the "facts." In physics the concept of the symbol has become, so to speak, as Ernst Cassirer has explained, "the centerpoint and focus of our entire epistemology." According to the French historian of physics, Duhem, the dividing line between physical theory and mere empiricism is the fact that there is no direct transition to physical knowledge from the empirical collecting and ordering of "facts." It is a matter of a *transgressus*, a transition, to a new perspective. Instead of the concrete data, we use symbolic images, "which are supposed to correspond to data on the basis of theoretical postulates which the observer considers as true and valid. . . . The *significance* of these concepts is not manifest in immediate perception, but can be determined and secured only by an extremely complex process of intellectual interpretation." [10] This conceptual interpretation represents the character of physical theory. In biological knowledge as well, it is necessary that the "creative power of imagination" should become effective. In my opinion, however, there is still a difference between physical and biological knowledge. The symbols which biology requires for the coherent representation of empirical facts must come closer to the "real" than is requisite for science of inorganic nature. This is due to the fact that, in the field of biology, knowledge and action are more intimately related than in physical science. Knowledge in biology always has to stand the test of usefulness. We do not want merely to understand the nature of an organism and to use our understanding secondarily for practical purposes; we are primarily interested in guaranteeing the existence of the living being, in helping it to live according to its nature and as well as possible. We need knowledge which will do justice to the whole organism, because in biology action always involves the individual as a whole. Mere reference to a part is insufficient. Even though an action may fit a part, it may distort the functioning of the whole. Therefore we cannot be satisfied with symbols which correspond only to part processes. We have to reject, for example, as we shall explain later, the scheme which serves as the basis of reflexology. We need symbols which are not as essentially alien to the observed phenomena as it is permissible for the symbols of physical science to be; in extreme cases physical science can confine itself to and content itself with a system of fictitious "signs." Biological knowledge also remains a set of symbols and deals with substitutes, it is true, but it does not make use of representation by simple arbitrary signs. Biological knowledge needs a more complete image, of an individual concrete character, which must match as closely as possible the particulars from which we build it up. After all, we do not regard the particular data we are studying as mere appearances, but as things which pertain to the reality of the whole organism, although they are insufficient for its direct cognition. Biological understanding, furthermore, can never be satisfied with finding laws of relationship between completely undetermined, theoretically assumed elements. In biology, symbols, theoretical representations, must in principle include quality and individuality in all their determinations. Biological descriptions must exhibit a definite qualitative organization; the symbol must have the character of a *Gestalt*. For this reason, though it is not unusual in physics, the assumption of various principles of explanation of the processes in an organism is untenable. In physics diverse systems of symbols may coexist and may be put to practical use at the same time. I am thinking here, for example, of the fact that the wave theory and the corpuscular conception in the light-quantum theory are both valid. Such a multiplicity of theories is not only theoretically tolerable for the physicist but does not necessarily obstruct his practical dealings. Yet such a procedure would not satisfy the requirements of biology.[11]

From these differences between physical and biological symbols it is understandable that, in spite of their agreement in basic procedure, physical science might find itself in opposition to the method of cognition here proposed. The contrast between the two sciences has often been apparent, and has led both to opposing tendencies within biology and to heated controversies between scientists. It is clear that, when based on the procedure we have chosen, our knowledge in the field of biology can never be final, and that we must content ourselves with an increasing approximation to the truth. This approximation must not be understood, however, in the sense of the approximate value of a mathematical series, which increases in correctness as we are able to determine decimal points, and where we can be satisfied with a limited number of decimals. It may be that biological knowledge frequently has a similar character, but in principle it is of an entirely different kind. Biological knowledge is not advanced by simply adding more and more individual facts. The facts which are gradually included in the "whole" as parts can never be evaluated merely quantitatively, in such a way that the more parts we are able to determine the firmer our knowledge becomes. In biology every fact always has a *qualitative* significance. Thus one single new fact may revolutionize an entire conception based on former findings, and demand an entirely new theory, in the light of which old facts may have to be newly evaluated. Final completeness and definiteness in biology is never possible unless one has recourse to explicit or non-explicit metaphysical interpretations, and these we have to reject as unempirical. Indeed, if one defines biology merely as the accumulation of single data, which must be secured by the analytic method, then he has to choose between two alternatives: either he renounces the type of understanding which grasps the organism as a whole — and in so doing virtually rescinds cognition in biology in general — or he resorts to metaphysical and speculative doctrines in order to supplement the body of his knowledge of the organism. Naturally we reject the latter procedure, although it has been frequently proposed in recent years, be it in the notion of vitalism, the idea of entelechy, or any kind of teleological approach.

Needless to say, the approach suggested here takes a fundamentally different course. Although this approach aims to attain knowledge of the nature of the organism by a method which deviates from the analytic-synthetic procedure, nevertheless it springs from the conviction that it offers the same objectivity and exactness as physical science. The claim of our approach to objectivity is grounded in the fact that it introduces as a working hypothesis an image of the organism as a whole, which is the supporting frame of reference for the determination of the factors that condition the phenomena that are within reach of our empirical observations. The claim of our approach to exactness is grounded in the fact that it is ready to shift its working hypotheses whenever new data demand a reorientation and reorganization, in order to fit in all the evidence of the phenomena observed.

Such an approach, of course, is ultimately tied up with the personality of the scientist. One man may

be convinced that the task of science is the accumulation of piecemeal data without any attempt at explanatory hypotheses, that this is the ethics of science. In that case he will content himself with the
stepwise procedure of cataloguing unrelated facts
ad infinitum. He achieves little for the understanding of nature, but he risks nothing. Another man
may believe that progress in science requires courage — the courage to advance explanatory hypotheses, to test them empirically, to expose them to
criticism, even to renounce and to revise them, if
necessary. There is risk in this, but the result —
satisfactory or unsatisfactory — meets the standards
of his ethical conviction that biology must strive
perpetually for adequate knowledge — the object
of its study, the living organism.

This point of view is not far removed from William James's idea about belief, which he advanced
not only in the field of religion but also in science.
Productive thinking, he says, presupposes belief:
"The same attitude of initial belief is necessary in
the case of specific theories and hypotheses, if we do
not want to content ourselves with a dogmatic
negation — as crudely dogmatic in its spirit and
method as any primitive taboo." [12] Certainly, belief
contains the danger of dogmatism. One may avoid
this, according to James and Perry, provided that
one combines belief "with a readiness to abandon the
hypothesis if after a period of trial the evidence is
negative." [13] Recognizing the similarity of my own
epistemological standpoint in biology to this attitude

toward cognition, I should like to add one thing. It is not sufficient to abandon a hypothesis after a period of trials with conflicting results. We can avoid error only if we are ready to give up our picture of the organism if *any* new phenomenon does not fit in with it, and if we try again and again to build up a new one through which all the given facts are understandable. We should not make auxiliary hypotheses; or, if we do, we must be conscious of doing so, aware of their transient character, and willing to give them up.

It may be difficult to see how the scientist can be convinced of the value of his scientific activities — and he must be so convinced in order to carry on his work — and at the same time aware of the possibility of being deceived, open-minded enough to see his own fallacies, and tolerant enough to confess that other people may be right. It may be difficult, I say, to believe that such contrary attitudes can be taken at the same time, but there is no doubt that it is possible, and I would say that the realization of that possibility is what makes a man a scientist. This attitude will not appear so strange if we realize that it corresponds very well to human nature, that it is characteristic of the approach of man to the world.

We shall see that our general concept of biological science is fruitful in connection with the special problem with which we have to deal in these lectures — human nature as seen in the light of experiences with sick people.

PATHOLOGY AND THE NATURE OF MAN

DURING the last few decades the use of the observation of patients with mental diseases for the understanding of normal human behavior has become more and more customary. For example, there was an attempt to make the behavior of primitive people intelligible in this way; the paintings and sculpture of primitive people were compared with the paintings and sculpture of the insane. By means of such comparisons the concept of a primitive, "archaic" form of thinking was developed.[1] I should also like to point out to what an extent the attempts to understand the cultural phenomena of early periods of mankind have been influenced by the psychoanalytic conception of neurosis. It is not necessary to discuss here the question of the relevance of these efforts. There is no doubt that they brought into focus many characteristics of human nature which before that had not been taken into consideration at all, or at least less than they deserved.

Before considering the phenomena observable in patients with mental diseases we must answer two questions: (1) Is it not dangerous to use pathological phenomena for formulating ideas about normal human nature? (2) Why do we use observations of pathologically changed human beings? What is the advantage of that procedure as compared with the use of the observation of normal persons?

In regard to the danger involved in using pathological phenomena, if one considers pathological facts — as has very often been done — as curiosities caused by illness and therefore not intelligible in the same way as the behavior of normal individuals, opposition to the use of pathological findings for the understanding of normal behavior is justified. There is no doubt, however, that such an assumption is false. If it were correct, we should not have the systematic statements about pathological facts that we do have; we should not even be able to describe them satisfactorily. Pathological phenomena are of a kind accessible to the understanding of the normal person. They are performances which have been modified according to definite laws, and they become intelligible if one takes into consideration the characteristic alterations which illness produces. To be sure, we are not able at present to understand all pathological phenomena from such a point of view, and those which are not understandable should not occupy the psychologist.

Here we shall deal only with phenomena of the understandable type. For this reason we shall choose a special kind of patient as a basis for our discussion. It is quite usual, particularly in textbooks of psychopathology, to start from observations of mentally ill persons, of psychotics and neurotics. We shall not omit evidence which can be gained from such cases, but this material will not constitute our main source. It is too complicated, and it still resists unambiguous analysis. In all discussions of this material one finds much theory and very little real evidence, very few real facts. Another type of patient provides better material, allows of better observation and much better understanding and explanation of modifications in behavior — the patient with an organic defect of the brain caused by injury or disease.[2]

We shall first take into consideration patients with circumscribed lesions of the brain cortex, in whom the damaged brain process has healed but with some irreparable defect. We begin with these cases instead of with patients who have acute illnesses, because in acute stages of illness (stages in which the struggle of the organism with the damage has not ended) the behavior picture is much more complicated, and it is much more difficult to analyze and to form an opinion of the changes that occur. We shall not overlook this acute condition, however, for we can also learn very much from it, particularly about the struggle of the organism against the damage done to it.

A great part of my own material has come from brain injuries incurred during the first World War. These injuries were very well suited for study, because they occurred in young people in good general physical condition. Furthermore, we had the unusual opportunity of being able to observe our

patients for a very long period of time, some for more
than eight years, in a relatively favorable environment. These circumstances gave us a much better
insight into behavior than it is possible to obtain with
patients who have brain lesions that are due to other
causative factors, though the examination of the
latter has not been omitted and has led us to the
same conclusions.

For those phenomena with which we have to
deal first the special localization of the lesion in the
brain cortex is relatively unimportant.[3] The phenomena are especially clear in lesions of the frontal
lobe, and therefore we shall take our examples especially from patients with lesions of this part of the
brain.[4]

However, to come back to our two questions, why
use pathological findings for understanding normal
behavior? The answer is that we try to learn from
the observation of sick people because we can acquire better information in this way, and acquire it
more easily, than by observing normal individuals.
Normal life is determined by so many factors, and
these factors are interwoven in such various and
complicated ways, that very often the reaction of a
normal organism even to an apparently simple stimulation is exceedingly difficult, sometimes quite impossible, to analyze and to understand. Now the greater
the defect of the organism, the simpler are its
responses to stimuli, and therefore the easier to
understand. Furthermore, pathological behavior is

particularly revealing concerning the organization of behavior. The destruction of one or another substratum of the organism gives rise to various changes in behavior, showing how these substrata and forms of behavior are interrelated and giving an insight into the organization of the total organism. Just as it is easier to gain an insight into the organization of performances in sick people, so it is easier to understand their ways of adjusting to changing conditions. For the sick organism, to find an adjustment to the abnormal condition produced by sickness is a question of being or not being. Thus we have an especially good opportunity of observing the forms and rules of adjustment, which are not always easily observed in normal persons.

The changes to be observed in patients with brain lesions are manifold, and concern both mental and bodily performances. Even if we restrict ourselves to mental performances we are faced with a very complex picture. Usually the disturbances have been described as separate changes in single fields of performance, as in perception, action, speech, emotions, memory, etc. Researches in the last few decades have shown more and more, however, that these complex pictures can be understood only if we regard them as expressions of a change in the total personality of the patient concerned.

We shall consider our findings in reference to two problems: first we shall concentrate on the change in personality; then on the adaptation of the patient to his defect. The study of the change of personality will give us some insight into the organization of the personality of the normal human being. The study of adaptation of the patient to his defect will inform us about the way the normal person comes to terms with the outer world. There would be no better way of getting to the heart of our problem than to give demonstrations with actual patients; I regret very much that this is impossible and that I must confine myself to a description of the behavior of certain patients.

The patient whom I have first in mind is a man thirty years of age, with a lesion of the frontal lobe. His customary way of living does not seem to be very much disturbed. He is a little slow; his face is rather immobile, rather rigid; his attention is directed very strictly to what he is doing at the moment — say, writing a letter or speaking to someone. Confronted with tasks in various fields, under certain conditions he gives seemingly normal responses, but under other conditions he fails completely in tasks that are apparently very similar to those he has performed quite well. These differences will be the starting point of our discussion. We shall ask: What is the reason for the failure in the one situation, the correct performances in the others?

Let us take as an example the behavior of this patient in a simple test. We place before him a small wooden stick in a definite position, pointing, for example, diagonally from left to right. He is asked to note the position of the stick carefully. After a half minute's exposure the stick is removed; then it is handed to the patient, and he is asked to put it back in the position in which it was before. He grasps the stick and tries to replace it, but he fumbles; he is all confusion; he looks at the examiner, shakes his head, tries this way and that, plainly uncertain. The upshot is that he cannot place the stick in the required position. He is likewise unable to imitate other simple figures built up of sticks. Next we show the patient a little house made of many sticks, a house with a roof, a door, a window, and a chimney. When he is asked to reproduce the model, he succeeds very well.

If we ask what the reason may be for the difference in the behavior of the patient in the two tasks, we can at once exclude defects in the fields of perception, action, and memory. For there is no doubt that copying the house with many details demands a greater capacity in all these faculties, especially in memory, than putting a single stick into a position seen shortly before.

At first sight the difference may seem inexplicable, but the following experiment clarifies the situation. We put before the patient two sticks placed together so as to form an angle with the opening pointing upward. The patient is unable to reproduce this model. Then we confront him with the same angle, the opening pointing down this time, and now he reproduces the figure very well at the first trial. When we ask the patient how it is that he can reproduce the second figure but not the first one, he says: "This one has nothing to do with the other one." Pointing to the second one, he says, "That is a roof"; to the first, "That is nothing."

These two replies lead us to an understanding of the patient's behavior. His first reply makes it clear that, to him, the two objects with which he has to deal are totally different from one another. The second answer shows that he apprehends the angle pointing downward as a concrete object out of his own experience, and he constructs a concrete thing with the two sticks. A concrete apprehension and concrete behavioral action are sufficient to meet the conditions of this test. In the former test the two sticks did not arouse an impression of a concrete thing. He had to conceive of the positions of two meaningless sticks in a meaningless connection with each other. He had to regard the sticks as mere representations indicating directions in abstract space. Furthermore, he had to keep these directions in mind and rearrange the sticks from memory as representatives of these abstract directions.

In the second test the patient needs to deal simply with a known concrete object; in the first he must give an account to himself of relations in space, and act on the basis of abstract ideas. Thus we may conclude that the failure of the patient in the first test lies in the fact that he is unable to perform a task which can be executed only by means of a grasp of the abstract. The test in which the opening of the angle points down does not demand this, and the patient is able to execute it perfectly. It is for the same reason that he is able to copy the little house, which seems to us to be much more complicated.

Some examples of performances by another patient — a woman with a disease of the frontal lobe [5] — may illustrate this defect still more clearly. This patient was also able to copy the angle pointing upward, and an analysis of her procedure revealed that this model was recognized by her as a concrete known object, namely, as a V. She was unable to copy a square, and it was obvious that this figure did not mean anything to her. However, she could copy the following model:

Asked what it was, she explained: it was a window. It could be demonstrated by many examples that if she recognized a model presented to her as a concrete object she could always copy it; if not, she failed. When she was unable to copy a model because it did not mean anything to her, she sometimes changed it so that it assumed for her the characteristics of a concrete object, and then she was able to copy it. Faced with a square

she produced the following picture:

When asked what these figures meant, she answered, "The windows of a church." She drew not meaningless squares but three church windows in a position in which they might actually be found; apparently where we see an abstract geometrical figure, she had seen a concrete object.

This lack of an attitude toward the abstract is found not only in such tests as we have mentioned but also in the behavior of the patient in general. Thus, for instance, the patient is unable to execute everyday activities if the latter demand an attitude toward the imaginary. For example, he may be able to perform expressive movements (say, the act of threatening) in situations to which they belong but is unable to demonstrate them outside of the situation which demands them. He is unable simply to demonstrate. He may have no difficulty in using known objects in a situation that requires them, but he is totally at a loss if he is asked to demonstrate the use of such an object outside of the concrete situation, and still more so if he is asked to do it without the real object. For example, one of our patients was able to drink water normally out of a glass, but if he was given an empty glass and asked to demonstrate how one brings the glass to the mouth in drinking and to make the appropriate movements with his mouth, he was unable either to do so or to imitate the action after it had been demonstrated to him.

There is a real gradation of difficulty in these various procedures, depending on the degree of concreteness in the action. The easiest performance is to drink during dinner, if one is thirsty. Under these very concrete conditions only patients with the very greatest impairment of function fail; if the impairment is less marked, the patient may fail if he has to drink, let us say, not at mealtime or if he is not thirsty, but simply on demand. If he is asked to demonstrate how to drink with an empty glass or without a glass — that is, in a situation involving a very high degree of abstraction — he is unable to do it at all. The reason why the patient's capacity for performing these steps corresponds somewhat to the degree of impairment of function is that his capacity for abstraction is disturbed by this to a greater or lesser degree.

Let us consider some other examples. The patient is asked to drive a nail with a hammer into a piece of wood. He takes the nail and drives it correctly by successive strokes of the hammer. Now the nail is taken away, and he is asked to imagine that there is a nail and that he is to drive it in. But this he is incapable of doing. He does not seem to know how to make the movement of driving it in either with the fist or with the hammer. Furthermore, even if he sees the nail and has the hammer in his hand, he is unable to make the movement of driving the nail in when he is not allowed to touch it.

The patient is asked to blow away a slip of paper. He does this very well. If the paper is taken away, and he is asked to think that there is a slip of paper and blow it away, he is unable to do so. Here again the situation is not realistically complete. In order to perform the task the patient would have to imagine the piece of paper there. He is not capable of this.

The patient is asked to throw a ball into boxes situated respectively at distances of three, nine, and fifteen feet. He does it quite well. When he is asked how far the several boxes are from him, he is not only unable to answer this question but unable even to say which box is nearer, which farther.

What is the difference between the two tasks? In the first, the patient has only to deal with objects in a behavioral fashion. It is unnecessary for him to be conscious of his act and of objects in a world separated from himself. In the second, however, he must separate himself from objects in the outer world and give himself an account of his actions and of the space relations in the world facing him. Therefore he fails.

That we do not have to deal here with a disturbance of space perception may be illustrated by another example which shows clearly that these patients are able to deal with complicated space relations when there is the possibility of doing it in a concrete way but fail as soon as an attitude toward the abstract is necessary.

In a conversation a patient was asked what she had been doing during the day. She answered, "I have been working." When asked where, she offered to lead the way to the workroom situated on an upper floor of the hospital. She went directly across the floor to the end of the ward, where there was a closed door, and glanced at the nurse, apparently realizing that the door was locked and desiring her to open it. The patient opened the door with a key given to her, locked it from the outside, returned the key to the nurse, went straight to the elevator situated on the other side of the corridor, rang correctly, and entered it on its arrival. On reaching the floor of the workroom she left the elevator at the direction of the operator, went directly to the door of the workroom, and immediately took her place at the table. She then asked the supervisor of the workroom for her needlework, prepared her material, and started to knit. All this was done without the least hesitation, even with alacrity. Later she was asked to go back to the ward. She arose and left, taking the correct route out and heading for the elevator. When she was stopped before reaching it, however, and was led into the corridor on the same floor (which was identical in structure with the floor on which her ward was located), she believed it to be the floor where her ward was. She then walked through the corridor as if she were on the ward floor and turned to the right at the end of the corridor as though she were about to enter her sleeping room. She was surprised to find herself in a room unknown to her. When told that she was on the wrong floor she became perplexed and looked around but was unable to find the correct way to the ward. She not only was ignorant of where she was but did not know how to return to the elevator. When, on another occasion, she was allowed to go straight to the ward, she did it in the same correct way as on her trip to the workroom. Plainly, she was able to take a complicated path in the same way as a normal person, but she failed immediately when the task demanded that she give herself an account of it — that is, of relations in space, the way from one place to another, etc. This may be deduced also from the fact that she could not describe the route, although she had followed it correctly.

We find in patients of this kind a similar modification of their attitude toward time; that is, they can tell us about certain aspects of temporal things, but they do not really know what they mean. They cannot really distinguish between different durations;

they do not understand the meaning of longer and shorter time. So far as their behavior is concerned, indeed, one would get the impression that they are quite at home in matters of chronology. For example, one patient was required repeatedly to present himself for an examination at four o'clock. He had a journey of three-quarters of an hour from his house to the hospital. He always arrived with the greatest punctuality. How did he manage it? He knew it would take him forty-five minutes. He knew that in order to be at the hospital at four o'clock he must leave his house at a quarter past three. This knowledge was conveyed to him by a certain position of the hands of his watch, without his knowing or needing to take into account their meaning in a general way.

Though such patients show an apparently normal ability to use a watch, nonetheless they have no sense of time at all. This is revealed by a simple test, such as asking them to say where the minute hand of a clock is at a certain time — for example, at thirteen minutes past four o'clock. A normal person would immediately say, "Slightly beyond the hour figure two." Our patients could not give a description at all, or could reach it only when allowed to point at the minutes from sixty to thirteen.

As a further example from another performance field we may choose a simple reaction test. The patient is instructed to execute a simple movement in response to an abruptly flashed light signal. After

some practice he learns the situation. He reacts correctly in a relatively short time. We now flash a red
light, then a blue light; and the patient is instructed
to execute the movement on seeing the red light but
to do nothing on seeing the blue. In this and similar
selective reactions his performance is inadequate.
He seems to become confused, and either does not
react at all or makes many errors. What is the
difference between the two tests? In one the patient
has to react in a simple way to a simple stimulus.
His behavior is simple and directly determined by the
stimulus. In the second test he has to *choose*. This
means that he has to face two possibilities; in other
words, he has to transcend the given situation, and
here is the very thing he cannot do.

These and similar examples show that the patient
is unable to deal with any merely "possible" situation at all. Thus we may also describe the deficiency
in these patients as a lack of capacity for approaching a "possible" situation.

Results with another task in quite a different field
yield confirmation. A simple story is read to the
patient. He seems unable to understand it. He may
repeat some single words, but he does not understand
their meaning and is unable to grasp the essential
point. Now we read him another story, which would
seem to a normal person to be no easier to understand. This time he understands the meaning very
well and recounts the chief points. What was the
difference between the two stories? The first one

dealt with a simple situation, but a situation which had no connection with the actual environment of the patient. The second story had a direct bearing on his own situation. Again we observe that the failure is due to an incapacity to approach a situation presented only in imagination. Choosing stories with this point of view, we are able to predict beforehand which ones the patient will be able to understand.

The same difficulty is observable in tests with graphic representations. Pictures of single objects are almost always recognized. In pictures which contain a number of things and persons in contact with each other, the patient may pick out some details, but he is unable to understand the picture as a whole and is unable to react in response to the whole. A precise examination reveals that the patient's real understanding does not depend on the greater or smaller number of components in a picture but on whether the components, whatever their number, hang together concretely and in ways familiar to him, or whether an understanding of their connection requires a more abstract synthesis on his part. In the first case the patient may apprehend pictures with many details. In the second he may lack understanding even if there are only a few details. If the picture does not reveal its essence directly, by bringing the patient into the situation which it represents, he is not able to recognize it. Thus one may characterize the deficiency as an inability to discover the essence of a situation.

This change in behavior finds its expression in characteristic changes in memory and attention. Under certain circumstances the faculty for the reproduction of facts acquired long ago may be normal. For example, things learned in school may be recalled very well in some situations, but not in all. The situation must reawaken old impressions. The patient must be able to regard the present situation in such a way that facts from the past belong to it. If this is not the case, he is completely unable to recall facts which he has reproduced very well in another situation. Repeated observation in many different situations demonstrates clearly that such memory failures are not caused by an impairment of memory content but by a failure in the approach that is requisite for a specific test. The patient has the material in his memory, but he is unable to use it freely; he can use it only in connection with a definite concrete situation, to which it must seem to him to belong. Only in this way, too, is he able to learn new facts. He may be able to learn numbers, syllables, or movements by heart; he is able to hold in memory situations, facts connected with his environment, and so on, but he is able to do so only in a concrete situation, and he can reproduce them only in the situation in which he learned them.

That such patients keep in mind essentially those patterns which they are able to comprehend — that is, grasp in a concrete way — the following simple example may illustrate. We put before a patient a single vertical line, or a circle or a square alone. She is able to copy each figure. Now we present the vertical line, the circle, and the square together. When asked to reproduce the patterns a minute later, the patient draws only the square; the others she has not held in mind. She apparently remembers only the one among several patterns which is a *concrete* figure for her — that is, the square, which she interprets as a window of a church. Obviously, her memory of an object is determined by the concreteness or abstractness of the object in question. Her ability to copy pictures is not bad if the pictures are seen by her as concrete figures.

We arrive at the same result in testing attention. At one time the patient appears inattentive, at another attentive, even abnormally so. Attention is usually weak in special examinations, particularly at the beginning, before the patient has gained the real approach to the whole situation. In such a situation he ordinarily seems much distracted. If he enters into the situation, however, his attention may be satisfactory, sometimes even abnormally keen. Under these circumstances he may be totally untouched by other stimuli from the environment to which normal persons will react unfailingly. His attitude, in short, depends upon whether he is equal to the task set him or not. In some tests he will always seem distracted — for example, in those which demand a change of approach (a choice reaction), because he is incapable of making a choice. Consequently, it is not correct to speak of a change of attention in these patients in terms of plus or minus. The state of the patient's attention is but a part of his total behavior and is to be understood only in connection with it.

The lack of an ability to grasp the abstract impairs all voluntary activities. Our patients have the greatest difficulty in starting any performance which is not determined directly by external stimuli. Thus, for example, they may be unable to recite the series of numbers on demand, although they are able to do it if the examiner begins the series. This difficulty finds its expression in a marked lack of initiative. They have great trouble in voluntary shifting, in switching over voluntarily from one topic to another, or from one part of a situation to another. Consequently they fail in performances in which such a shift is necessary. Since, as we have shown, they are hindered in the making of choices, they are unable to follow a conversation between various people, especially if the contents change, and they seem rigid and lifeless, mentally and bodily, in everything they do.

This difficulty in voluntary shifting can be explained in the following way. Shifting presupposes that I have in mind simultaneously the object to which I am reacting at the moment and the one to which I am going to react. One is in the foreground, the other in the background. But it is essential that the object in the background be there as a possible object for future reaction. Only then can I change from the one to the other. This presupposes the capacity for approaching things that are only imagined, "possible" things, things which are not given in the concrete situation. If, for example, we normal people do not understand a complicated picture immediately, we voluntarily look first at this and then at that part; we keep changing our attitude until we achieve success. This changing presupposes the capacity for freeing oneself from a concrete situation and turning to something that is already in mind. The mentally sick man is incapable of doing either because of his inability to grasp what is abstract.

To be sure, we normal people do not always shift in an arbitrary manner. Shifting may be directed by the changing significance of one part or another for the best and most adequate performance, and this happens somewhat passively. But if the situation itself does not bring about this change we can focus voluntarily upon one part or another. Normal performances usually demand both active and passive shifting. Among the abnormal, the incapacity for voluntary shifting makes the fulfillment of certain tasks impossible.

We have already mentioned the fact that our patients are unable to imitate or copy anything that is not a part of their immediate concrete experience. It is a very interesting expression of this incapacity that they have the greatest difficulty in repeating a sentence which is meaningless for them — that is, the contents of which do not correspond to the reality they are capable of grasping. Thus a patient of mine was unable to repeat such sentences as "The snow is black." I was able to induce him to repeat the individual words, isolated, and then to repeat the words one after the other in the correct succession, but he stopped before he spoke the word "black," looked startled, and said, "white," or, if he said the word "black," he did it very quickly and apparently with great uneasiness, and then said very quickly afterwards, "white." To say such things apparently requires the assumption of a very difficult attitude. It demands, so to speak, the ability to live in two spheres, the concrete sphere where "real" things take place and the non-concrete, the merely "possible" sphere, for in saying meaningless things we must shift from one to the other. This the patient is unable to do. He can live and act only in the concrete sphere. He is therefore always himself. He is unable to place himself in the situation of other people; he is not able to imitate other people, nor is he able to impersonate as an actor is.

His inability to put himself in another's place finds its expression in certain characteristics of his emotional and social behavior. He frequently exhibits a dulling of the emotions, but in other situations he does not appear to be without feeling; on the contrary, we observe in him a great excitability. If we analyze both situations carefully, we find that the presence or absence of emotional expression corresponds to his entire behavior in a given situation, and that his emotional behavior is best understood in terms of his attitude toward the situation. The fact seems to be this: If the patient does not seem to react emotionally in a satisfactory way, it is in situations in which he also fails to comprehend the essentials to which a definite feeling attaches. This frequently demands a grasp of the abstract. He may have grasped only a part of the situation because only that part could be grasped concretely. His reaction seems inappropriate to us because we regard the whole situation and not merely a part of it. If we consider his behavior from this point of view, we see that, in the situation as it is experienced by him, his feeling is not abnormal.

This also helps us to understand why it is that a patient who appears very dull may suddenly become excited in a situation which at first seems to contain no cause for irritation. For example, a patient of mine had a friend who was his close companion. One day the friend went to a cinema with another man. He did not take our patient because the latter had seen the picture before and would not go to see it a second time. When the friend came back our patient was in a state of great excitement and refused to speak to him. He was not to be quieted by any arguments. No explanation — that his friend did not want to offend him, that his friendship had not changed — made any impression. From that time on, our patient was his old friend's enemy.

This reaction, at first so unintelligible, can be understood if we remember that the patient was able to make only a direct concrete approach to any situation. This was the case in his approach to his friend. He saw only that his friend was the companion of another man, and he felt himself slighted. He was unable to understand that his friend's conduct in no way actually affected their relations. He could not understand why his friend went without him, and he could not perceive the situation as a whole. He saw only the concrete separation between himself and his friend, and his exaggeration is thoroughly understandable if we consider how difficult it is, in the case of such a change of attitude, to enter into the relation of friendship. The patient felt his loneliness, and sank into a "catastrophic situation" of confusion and anxiety.* He regarded his friend as the cause of his bad condition and reacted to him in a way that is easily understandable in terms of his grasp of the situation.

It is in general very difficult for our patients to come into close contact with other people. They do not try to become intimate friends with other persons or to mingle in society; as a rule they live in an isolated way. Only a concrete situation by which they are affected brings them into and keeps them in contact with others; then their feelings may correspond to normal feelings. Outside the actual situation, however, they may be without any inner contact with

* Cf. p. 86.

the members of their society. An example may make
this clear. One of our patients never seemed to be
concerned about his family. He never spoke of his
wife or children, was unresponsive when we ques-
tioned him about them, and when it was suggested
to him that he should write to his family was utterly
indifferent. Thus he appeared to lack all feeling.
Now it was an established practice that at times he
should visit his home, which was situated in another
town, and stay there several days. While at home
he conducted himself, as we learned, like a normal
man in the bosom of his family. He was kind and
affectionate to his wife and children, and interested
in their affairs in so far as his abilities would permit.
Yet after his return to the hospital from such a visit,
upon being asked about his people, he would smile
in an embarrassed way and give evasive answers;
he seemed utterly estranged from his home situation.
Unquestionably what ailed this man was not really a
deterioration of his character on the emotional and
moral side. Rather, he could not represent the home
situation to himself, and consequently the corresponding feelings did not arise. This lack of real
contact with others, taken in connection with the
impairment of a grasp of the abstract, will give us a
basis for our discussion of the social relationship in
normal persons.

We have characterized the patient's deficiency in
different terms — as lack of a grasp of the abstract,
lack of an approach to imagined things, inability to

give himself an account of his own acting or thinking, inability to make a separation between the ego
and the world, and lack of freedom. At bottom all
these terms, and others which one may use to characterize the facts, mean basically the same thing.
We speak, in brief, of the lack of an attitude toward
the abstract.[6]

To avoid misunderstanding, let me say here that
the perception of concreteness by different patients
need not be expressed in the same way in a given
task. What is concrete for one individual can only
be understood within the frame of reference for that
particular patient, as it is related to his pre-morbid
individuality and his changed capacity and the situation given. Therefore it may express itself in different ways in different patients with the same type
of lesion.

I know that the designation of the two kinds of
behavior as "abstract" and "concrete" is misunder-
standable and has often been misunderstood. I am
sorry that I do not know any more appropriate words
with which to characterize the facts. Now I am very
anxious not to be misunderstood at this point because what I am about to say concerns the most
important problem in our attempt to characterize
human nature on the basis of our findings.

Thus I should like to review briefly what has been
said. In "concrete" performances a reaction is determined directly by a stimulus, is awakened by all
that the individual perceives. The individual's pro-

cedure is somewhat passive, as if it were not he who
had the initiative. In "abstract" performances an
action is not determined directly and immediately
by a stimulus configuration but by the account of the
situation which the individual gives to himself. The
performance is thus more a primary action than a
mere reaction, and it is a totally different way of
coming to terms with the outside world. The individual has to consider the situation from various
aspects, pick out the aspect which is essential, and
act in a way appropriate to the whole situation.
True, this procedure may have various degrees of
complexity. Sometimes the situation demands nothing more than a singling out of one property of an
object, as, for instance, when we are asked to sort
objects according to their colors. In the highest
degree of complexity we have not only to apprehend
objects by means of certain simple characteristics
but to choose aspects for consideration in accordance
with a certain task which demands a conceptual
organization. Even in its simplest form, however,
abstraction is separate in principle from concrete
behavior. There is no gradual transition from the
one to the other. The assumption of an attitude
toward the abstract is not more complex merely
through the addition of a new factor of determination; it is a totally different activity of the organism.
Perhaps it would be better not to designate both
conditions by the term "behavior," since behavior
connotes real activity and is especially well suited

to the concrete performance. Abstraction represents, rather, a preparation for activity; it involves an attitude, i.e., an inner approach, which leads to activity. Therefore it is better to speak of an attitude toward the abstract. Real action is never abstract; it is always concrete. The difference between the two conditions is shown in the difference between the processes which precede action. In the concrete situation action is set going directly by the stimuli; in the situation involving the abstract, action is begun after preparation which has to do with a consideration of the whole situation.

Yet these explanations are not entirely correct. From them it might seem as if concrete behavior could take place in complete independence of the abstract attitude, determined by the external situation alone. This, however, is not the case. The arousal and the normal course of an action presuppose in any case an abstract attitude. In normal life we are rarely forced into action by the stimulus situation itself. Usually we have to place ourselves — at least in imagination — in the appropriate situation. The outside world merely gives us the impulse to do this. Thus even the initiation of an action demands the abstract attitude. Nor is the latter entirely excluded during the performance of a concrete act. On the contrary, the concrete performance is always somewhat dependent upon the abstract attitude, which becomes effective in restoring order as soon as any disturbance in the normal course of concrete performances occurs. Thus concrete performances are grounded upon the abstract attitude in their initiation and receive its regulative control during their course.

This is very evident in our patients. Their concrete behavior can begin only if it is stimulated by the outer world, and it is to an abnormal degree dependent upon the outer world. It runs in an abnormal, compulsive way, and is disturbed very easily by changes in external events. It lacks spontaneity and, so to speak, an adequate context within the individual.

From what we have said it is clear that normally we do not distinguish sharply between performances carried out on the basis of the abstract attitude and those carried out in a concrete way. Normal performance demands both kinds of behavior. If I stress the importance of the abstract attitude for normal human beings, I do not mean that normal performances — or even the larger part of them — are carried out only in the abstract way. In ordinary life concrete behavior plays a very great role; most of our everyday performances are of this sort. Many performances consist of parts, some of which demand the one, others the other behavior.

Whether abstract attitude or concrete behavior plays a more prominent role depends upon various factors — first, on the situation. There are situations in which most normal persons react in a very concrete way without thinking about their behavior.

A person enters his bedroom in the evening and puts on the light without realizing that he is doing so. Here and in similar cases our actions are determined directly by stimuli. But even here we do not act without employing an abstract attitude to a certain extent. We are acting somewhat passively, but we are not forced to act in this way. Under certain conditions we can go to bed without putting on the light — if, for instance, we want to avoid disturbing someone else. This shows that, even where we react in a very concrete direct way, our actions are determined somewhat by our general mental set — that is, by some abstract attitude. Thus even in very familiar everyday actions we have to deal with a combination of abstract and concrete behavior.

The same is the case in activities of such high rank as scientific and artistic work. Perfection in any field demands the concrete execution of at least some parts of our actions without our thinking about them. Thinking itself is very often just such a concrete process; one thought involuntarily brings about another. The same is true in artistic expression. In all productivity concrete action plays a very great role. We must stress the point, however, that productive action is never possible unless it is embedded in an abstract set. The importance of concrete behavior in artistic creativeness has perhaps been overemphasized. Creative work can never be produced without an ideational basis — that is, without the abstract attitude. In this respect nothing in our patients is so impressive as their lack of productiveness.

In this connection it may be said that any comparison of the artistic products of abnormal persons with those of normal artists, however many the similarities, have a very uncertain basis.[7] In any case, we ought to be much more careful in our judgments about the artistic products of the insane than we have often been. The point must be stressed that the products in question stem mainly from schizophrenics, and as a result of new investigations by Vigotski, Hanfmann and Kasanin, Bolles and Goldstein, we now know that schizophrenics suffer from an impairment of the abstract attitude.

The role which this attitude plays in the life of an individual depends further upon the latter's individual organization, his constitutional and mental type. There are some persons who are more strongly directed toward the concrete than the abstract, and others who prefer by nature to assume an abstract attitude in all their doings. Thus one may easily arrive at a wrong judgment about the importance of the abstract attitude for human behavior by the observation that very intelligent people seem to behave very concretely. Behavior in performance tests provides a case in point. Take, for example, the following simple test, which I devised for this purpose with the material of the Kohs blocks.[8]

The subject is faced with various simple designs and is asked to reproduce them with cubes, each cube having a different color on each side. The cubes are of the same size as the entire design. Thus the product built up from the blocks is four times as big as the model. On first looking at the models one is impressed by certain figures which stand out, and one may try to reproduce them. With this procedure, however, one can be at most only partially successful. One has to abstract from the outstanding figures, divide the model in imagination into squares corresponding to the blocks, and copy the divided pictures. Our patients fail in various ways because of the impairment of their ability to abstract: they cannot abstract from the size or from the figures given, and they are not able to divide the model into squares in imagination. Now we sometimes observe in normal people behavior similar to that of our patients. Sometimes it takes a long time before a subject gets the idea of dividing the model in imagination, and sometimes the examiner has to demonstrate the successful procedure. This may suggest that intelligent normal persons, like our patients, are very concrete in their reactions and that the capacity for abstracting cannot be so essential as we have asserted. Yet there is one great difference between these normal persons and our patients which shows that such assumption is wrong. Immediately after a demonstration by the examiner the normal individual is able to continue in the correct way. This proves that he has grasped the abstract method and is following it. But a demonstration of the abstract method does not help our patients at all. They really lack the abstract attitude which normal persons possess. Although normal persons may have a tendency to behave primarily in the concrete manner and often begin in this way, they can shift very easily to the other mode of procedure and so gain the insight that is necessary for success.

Thus these and similar observations of normal people do not affect our conception of the significance of the abstract attitude; they show only that there are two types of normal persons — one that prefers the more concrete behavior, and another that prefers the abstract. This difference reveals a characteristic which has to be taken into consideration in any analysis of the structure of the personality, but it does not reveal any essential difference in the organization of various human beings. We shall have to come back to these differences in personality when we speak about the structure of the personality.

Normal behavior is characterized by an alternation between an attitude involving abstract and one involving concrete behavior, and this alternation is appropriate to the situation and the individuality, to the task for which the organism is set. If either attitude becomes independent and governs the behavior of a normal person too completely, then we are faced with an anomalous form of behavior. This we shall discuss later.

To the characteristic deviation of behavior from the normal shown in the various examples I have given, there naturally corresponds a change in the world in which the patient lives. We may say that the patient has no world at all outside himself and opposed to him, in the sense that we do: he is impaired in his capacity for separating himself from the world which surrounds him; he is embedded in his own world. His inability to achieve performances which demand an abstract attitude means not only a shrinkage of his personality but also a shrinkage of the world in which he lives. In addition, not only are the contents of his environment diminished, and his own capacities shrunken, but there is a decrease in his freedom of action.

Perhaps we are now justified in drawing some conclusions as to the structure of the normal human being. We may start from this point: In the type of cases we have used as a basis for our discussion we never observe that an impairment of concrete behavior occurs while the attitude toward the abstract remains intact. The attitude toward the abstract is always impaired first, and to a higher degree. Now we may assume that those capacities which are first impaired by a brain lesion are those which demand the best functioning of the most complicated substratum of the brain. Thus it is not accidental that we find the loss of this capacity especially in lesions of the frontal lobe, which we consider to be the most complex part of the human brain. Further, we may assume that the performances corresponding to the best functioning of the most complex part of the brain are the most important — that is, represent the highest capacity of the organism in question. Thus we are led to the conclusion that we must distinguish in the human being two types of behavior, the concrete and the abstract, and that abstract behavior represents the highest capacity — in fact, the essential capacity — of the human being.

III

THE ABSTRACT ATTITUDE
AND SPEECH

THE IMPAIRMENT of the abstract attitude is clearly revealed in characteristic changes in the speech of patients with brain lesions. We know various forms of speech defects in such patients and usually class them together as aphasia.[1] No other pathological material can teach us so much about the organization of the human being. Since we cannot deal with all the various types of aphasia, I shall confine the discussion to a special form, known as amnesic aphasia,[2] which in my opinion is particularly well suited to give us an insight into the nature of man.

If one examines a patient with this type of aphasia one observes as a striking symptom that he is totally or partially unable to find names for concrete things. This is especially noticeable in cases where he has the task of naming presented objects, but it is also apparent in his spontaneous language, which is conspicuously lacking in nouns and verbs. Usually this symptom is considered as the characteristic change, but closer examination shows that other changes also occur. Many circumlocutions are used where we would use single words. A patient shown a cup, for example, may respond with, "This is for drinking,"

or say, on seeing a penholder, "That is for writing,"
etc. In another case, a patient of mine said, "That
is something for the rain," in a situation in which
we should merely say, "That is an umbrella." Or
she said: "I must have it for the rain," or, "I have
three umbrellas at home." In the last sentence she
used the right word in her periphrasis, yet she was
unable to repeat it in reply to a repeated question,
"What is that?" soon afterward. Evidently such a
patient has not lost the word itself but for some reason is unable to use it in naming an object. Further,
his entire behavior shows peculiarities. All his acting
and thinking seems to center, to an unusual degree,
around his own personality and its relation to the
world. He is acting in the world rather than thinking or speaking about it. His speech is accompanied
to a marked degree by expressive movements. Very
often we observe that he seems unable to express his
meaning by words but can do so quite well by movements.

The change involving the whole behavior appears
still more strikingly in special examinations. I shall
begin by presenting the results of one examination
with a sorting test because the results seem particularly well suited to carry us into the core of our
problem, namely, the basic change in patients with
amnesic aphasia.

We place before the patient a heap of colored
woolen skeins — Holmgren's well-known samples
used for testing color efficiency. We ask him to pick

out all the red skeins and put them together. (There are, of course, many different shades of red.) Or we pick out one particular skein — for example, a dark red one — and ask him to choose strands of the same and similar colors.

In the first task a normal person with good color efficiency usually selects a great number of different shades of the same ground color — that is, for example, different reds, without regard to intensity, purity, lightness, etc. In the same task patients with amnesic aphasia behave quite differently, and exhibit varying types of behavior. For example, when he is told to choose all the skeins that are similar to a given skein, one patient chooses only skeins of the very same or of a closely similar shade. Though urged to go on he chooses a small number because there are only a few very similar ones in the heap. Another patient matches a given bright shade of red with a blue skein of similar brightness. At first such a patient may seem to be color-blind, but it can be demonstrated beyond doubt that his color efficiency is normal and that he is able to differentiate very distinctly between colors that are much alike. More precise observations disclose that in this case the choice is determined by a particular color attribute of the given skein, its brightness. We observe, further, that the choice may be decided by a number of different attributes — at one time by brightness, at another by softness, or coldness, warmth, etc. However — and this is a very amazing thing — a patient

who seems to be choosing according to a certain attribute is not able to follow this procedure voluntarily
if it is demanded of him — that is, if he is asked to
choose only bright skeins, etc. Further, we observe
that he does not seem to be able to hold to a certain
procedure. He has chosen, for instance, some bright
skeins. Suddenly he begins selecting on the basis of
another attribute — the coldness of the color or some
other factor. In another case, the patient arranges
the skeins as if guided by a scale of brightness. He
begins with a very bright red, then adds one less
bright, and so on to a dull one. But if we ask him to
place the skeins in a succession according to their
brightness he shows himself incapable of the performance, even if it is demonstrated to him.

To understand the behavior of our patients, it is
necessary to examine the procedure of normal persons in such tasks. If we normal persons want to
choose a color, we select various nuances, even
though we see that they have various attributes not
equal to one another, because we recognize that they
belong together in respect to their *basic* quality. The
several shades are merely examples of this quality,
and we treat the skeins not as different individual
things but as representatives of that one basic color.
For the moment we ignore all differences in shade
and disregard all singular attributes. We are able to
do this because we can abstract and because we can
hold fast to a procedure once initiated.

There is another approach, however, which is open

to the normal person. We can start with one particular skein and move it about over the heap, *passively* surrendering ourselves to the impressions that emerge. Then either of two things will take place. If we find skeins resembling our sample in *all* attributes, all these immediately cohere in a unitary sensory experience with the sample. If we find skeins which match our sample in some respects, we experience a characteristic unrest concerning the heap, and an alternating sense of relationship between skeins in the heap and the sample, according to different attributes. No matter whether we experience rivalry or matching, the coherence we feel results directly from sense data and takes place passively; we do not experience a definite attitude toward any attribute.

There is an essential difference between the more passive kind of approach and the former, in which we definitely choose a particular color. In the one, a definite ordering principle determines our actions; in the other, there is no such principle, and our actions are passively determined by outer impressions. These two kinds of behavior correspond to what we have called abstract and concrete behavior and what we may now call categorical and concrete behavior.

A particular kind of language belongs to each of these types of behavior. Our behavior is abstract when we give a name to an object. When we speak of "table" we do not mean a special given table with all its accidental properties; we mean table in general. The word is used as a representative of the category "table" even when naming a particular table. Thus, if we are asked to group together all reds, upon hearing the word "red" we are immediately prepared to select colors in a categorical fashion. In this approach language plays a great role, and the particular form it takes here may be designated by Karl Buehler's term, *darstellende Sprache*, which may be translated as "representative speech."

In the second form of behavior language does not play much of a role at all. Our words merely accompany our acts and express a property of the object itself, like other properties, such as color, size, etc. This fact is shown in the particular kind of words we use in such situations. The words are especially adapted to the individuality of the given object. We use words like "rose-red," "violet"; we do not say "red," but "pink," "dark red," "strawberry-red," "sky-blue"; not green but "grass-green," etc. Often we have no word for naming a given object, and then we do it in a roundabout way. Words are used here less as representative of categories than as individual properties which, like other properties, belong to the object in question. We call such words "individual" words.

Now when we consider the behavior of the patient in the light of these elucidations we may say that it is similar to the second approach of normal persons. He is able to assume only the more concrete, the more realistic, attitude. Therefore he chooses identical skeins or skeins which are similar in an outstanding property, such as brightness. This interpretation finds confirmation in the greater concreteness of the patient's general behavior, in the predominance of acting over thinking, in the accompaniment of speech by expressive movements.

Our assumption is finally substantiated by the results of another type of sorting test. If a normal person tries to arrange a number of objects lying before him — say, on the writing table of a very busy man — he may do it in various ways, according to various attitudes. He may arrange them by size, by color, by function, by the importance of their situation, in terms of activity, of thought, etc. Further, he is able both to shift from one attitude and one kind of order to another as the situation demands it, and to effect a particular arrangement on demand. A patient with amnesic aphasia, confronted with miscellaneous objects with the instruction to group them, will exhibit the same behavior as in the color test. He is capable of proceeding only in a manner that indicates that he is guided by *concrete* promptings.

A particularly instructive example is the following. Among a number of different objects there were placed on a table before a patient a corkscrew and a bottle with a cork loosely set in its neck. The patient, asked to arrange these, did not put the bottle and the corkscrew together. Asked if these two objects did not belong together, he said, "No," very positively, backing his answer up with the explanation, "The bottle is already opened." Under these circumstances most normal people would pay no attention to the fact that the cork was not fast. For the immediate task — the grouping together of objects that belong together — it is quite incidental and unimportant whether the cork is loose or fast. With the abstract attitude, in a form of sorting which involves grouping objects according to categories, we assume that bottle and corkscrew belong together, independently of their occurrence in any particular situation. But for the patient who is able to take the objects only as they are given in sense experience, the corkscrew does not belong to the bottle and the cork if the cork is already loose. From this and similar cases it is plain that he takes the concrete attitude toward objects as well — we may say toward all objects, toward the world in its entirety.

Our conclusion is that the patient's inability to name objects is a consequence of his inability to assume the abstract attitude, for this is a prerequisite for the naming of objects. As we have shown in the example of the umbrella, he has not lost the words themselves, but he is unable to use them in situations which demand their use as categories. Often a patient, asked to name a color presented to him, calls out over and over various color names: red, blue, yellow, etc. He may even utter the appropriate name, but in spite of this he is still unable to connect it with the color itself. Furthermore, it does not help him when we say the different color names for him to repeat after us.

But what makes these words unsuitable for use in connection with objects in the normal way — that is, as names? Why can they not be used as symbols for objects? This may be disclosed in observations of patients who utter appropriate words in connection with some objects but, as closer analysis shows, do not use them in a normal categorical fashion. Here we learn that the patients have the same *concrete* attitude toward the words that they have toward objects they are asked to sort.

Asked to mention the names of several different kinds of animals, the patient may be at first unable to do so. In one case it was not until we had given a patient such examples as dog, cat, mouse, that she replied to the question at all. Then suddenly she said: "A polar bear; a brown bear; a lion; a tiger." Asked why she named these particular animals, she said, "If we enter the zoölogical gardens, we come at first to the polar bear and then to the other animals." [3] Obviously she had recalled the animals as they were situated in the zoölogical gardens, and had used the words only as belonging to the concrete situation, not as names for objects. It was very characteristic that she did not simply say "bear," a word which represents the category of all bears, and which we would use when asked to name animals, but that instead she selected the words "polar bear," "brown bear." The same fact appeared when the patient was asked to recite different female first names. She said: "Grete, Paula, Clara, Martha," and, asked why she had mentioned these particular names, answered, "These are all G——s" (G—— was her family name), and went on, "One sister died of a heart neurosis." The last sentence demonstrates very clearly that the patient did not recite names but only uttered words which belonged to a particular concrete situation, namely, to her family situation.

How very concretely such words are apprehended may be demonstrated by the following example. When, to such a patient of ours, a knife was offered with a pencil, she called the knife a "pencil sharpener"; when the knife was offered with an apple, it was to her an "apple parer"; when offered with a potato, it was a "potato peeler"; in company with a piece of bread, it became a "bread knife"; and with a fork it was "knife and fork." The word "knife" alone she never uttered spontaneously, and when she was asked, "Could we not always call it simply 'knife?'" she replied promptly, "No."

With different mental sets the same word may mean for the normal person different things. For example, in German the word *Anhänger* is used for a lavalier which hangs on a chain around a girl's neck, or for a follower of a personage, or for the second car which is customarily attached to a streetcar in Germany. Our patient was unable to use the word in more than one sense or in connection with more than one object. If she understood the word in a particular sense she could not understand that it could be used in another sense. This observation shows clearly that the words themselves are qualitatively different for such patients as compared with normal people, by whom the same word can be used for various totally different objects. By patients with amnesic aphasia they can be used only in a concrete way, for they seem to have lost the characteristic that is necessary if they are to be used in a categorical sense — that is, as symbols. They may be useful as properties belonging to a definite object, but they have become unfit to serve as symbols for ideas. *They have lost their meaning.*

It has usually been assumed, even by those authors who recognize that these patients have lost the categorical attitude toward objects, that the cause of this lack is the loss of words, or a difficulty in evoking words. This cannot be the case. There is no doubt that words provide a very important means of helping us to assume the categorical attitude and of stabilizing concepts, but, as we have explained, our patients have not really lost the words. Instead, the words have lost their character of being usable in the abstract, and this change in language is only one expression of the basic change in our patients, *the lack of the capacity to create any sort of abstraction.*

These observations are important for understanding the character of the capacity for naming objects. This apparently simple performance does not represent a superficial connection between a thing and a

word; naming objects presupposes the abstract attitude and is an expression of a very high mental function. But these observations reveal another point
still more important for our discussion. They show
that speech is one of the essential characteristics of
human nature, inasmuch as it is tied to man's highest
capacity, the capacity for abstract behavior.

Another significant point appears. The patients
we have been discussing have not lost the capacity
to use words in a concrete way, and from the advantage this type of speech gives them we can infer
what role it may play in normal life.

A patient of mine could name pure colors with
their respective color names — red, blue, and so on
— but she declined to extend the same word to the
several shades of a given color. The words were at
her disposal only as individual, concrete things belonging to definite objects. In the course of time,
after repeated examinations, she came to call various
shades by the same name; for instance, she would
use the word "red" for all shades of red. Superficially
she seemed to behave like a normal person. One
might have thought that she had improved, that she
had regained the meaning of the words. But it was
not so. Asked why she now called all these different
shades by the same word, she answered, "The doctors
have told me that all these colors are named red.
Therefore I call them all red." Asked if this was not
correct, she laughed and said, "Not one of these
colors is red, but I am told to call them by this word."

It is clear that she had not used the words as symbols but had learned to build a quite external connection between one word and a diversity of things, a quite meaningless connection, which, however, because she had a good memory, helped her to carry out a task, if only in a very external way.

Thus we must distinguish very definitely between two ways of using words in connection with objects: real naming, which is an expression of the categorical attitude toward the world in general, and pseudo-naming of objects, which is simply a use of words held in memory. The incidence of this pseudo-naming depends on the extent of the individual's verbal possessions. In it words are used as properties of objects just as other properties — color, size, hue — are used; they belong to concrete behavior. To this type of words belong the speech automatisms of ordinary people — the alphabet, numbers in series, the days of the week, and many other longer or shorter speech expressions of everyday life. This use of words plays a great role in ordinary speech. In learning a foreign language, for example, as long as we have no real conception of it as a language, we possess its words only by such superficial connections with the words of our own language. If we understand their meaning within the realm of the foreign language itself, then the words achieve an absolutely different character; then they become representative of a category.

Important as these speech possessions are for our

everyday language, they obtain their significance only from their position against a background of representational, meaningful speech. This may be gathered from the fact that to a certain extent speech automatisms are developed only if a human being possesses the function of meaning. Certainly a child acquires many automatisms by repeated imitation of his own speech and that of others. If he is not able to use them later in connection with meaningful speech, however, his learning of these words is limited, and he forgets many that he has learned. We know that children with an inborn deficiency in the attitude toward the abstract are not able to develop speech automatisms to any extent, and that they forget them, in spite of a good memory, if the words are not practiced constantly. In the same way, patients with a loss of categorical behavior may lose their speech automatisms if they are not continuously kept in use by the demands of concrete situations. Thus, for example, if the meaning of numbers is lost, these patients lose the ability to count and the knowledge of the simple multiplication table, which are usually regarded as well-established possessions of memory.

Speech automatisms may be designated as "tools," but it is false to consider language in general as a mere tool. Even speech automatisms are dependent upon the categorical attitude both in their building and in their use. This point is most important. The use of speech automatisms alone is not real language.

Our patients, despite their lack of the categorical attitude, may be able to use speech automatisms which they acquired at a time when they were capable of the categorical attitude, but the fact that their speech lacks the spontaneity and fluidity which characterizes normal language, and that they are not able to use the words as symbols, demonstrates very clearly that language without a categorical background is not real language. Whenever human beings use language to establish natural connections between themselves and the world, particularly with their fellow men, language is not merely a tool. It is not merely a superficial means of communication, not a simple naming of objects through words; it represents a particular way of building up the world — namely, by means of abstractions. "Language," said Wilhelm von Humboldt, "never represents objects themselves but the concepts which the mind has formed of them in the autonomous activity by which it creates language." It is this that makes language so important, so essential to the development of a culture. It becomes a manifestation both of all that is human, the human being at his deepest, and of man's psychic bond with his fellows; in none of his cultural creations does man reveal himself so fully as in the creation of language itself. It would be impossible for animals to create a language, because they do not have this conceptual approach toward the world. If they had, they would be not animals but human beings. Nothing brings this home to us

more strikingly than observing in patients with amnesic aphasia the parallelism between the changes
which occur in personality and the loss of the meaning of words.

ORDERED AND CATASTROPHIC BE-
HAVIOR: ANXIETY AND FEAR

THE FOREGOING lectures have given us some insight
into the organization of man by showing the consequences of the lack of the attitude toward the
abstract. In this lecture we shall try to gain an
understanding of the way in which men come to
terms with the outside world. In discussing this important problem we shall draw upon observations
of our patients' ways of adapting themselves to the
difficulties caused by their defects.

Let us begin with the observation of the behavior
of one of our patients in a task which seems very
simple.[1] We give him a problem in simple arithmetic
which before his sickness he would without any
doubt have been able to solve. Now he is unable to
solve it. But merely noticing and recording the fact
that he is unable to perform a simple multiplication
would be an exceedingly inadequate account of the
patient's reaction. By simply looking at him we discover a great deal more than his arithmetical failure.
He looks dazed, changes color, becomes agitated and
anxious, starts to fumble. A moment before, he was
amiable; now he is sullen and evasive or exhibits
temper. He presents a picture of a very much dis-

tressed, frightened person, a person in a state of anxiety. It takes some time to restore him to a state which will permit the examination to continue. In the presence of a task which he can perform, the same patient behaves in exactly the opposite manner. He looks animated and calm, and appears to be in a good mood; he is well-poised and collected, interested, coöperative; he is "all there." We may call the state of the patient in the situation of success *ordered behavior*; his state in the situation of failure, *disordered* or *catastrophic behavior*.[2]

In the catastrophic condition the patient not only is incapable of performing the required task, which exceeds his impaired capacity, but he also fails, for a longer or shorter period, in performances which he is able to carry out in the ordered state. The whole organism is in great disorder for some time. Observation of the patient over a longer period of time reveals that his behavior fluctuates between these two opposing states and that the catastrophic type of behavior appears very often in examinations. After a while the patient becomes calmer, and catastrophic situations more or less disappear, even if the disturbance of functions remains unaltered. In normal life as well, in his attempt to come to terms with the outer world, the individual has to go through such states of disorder or catastrophe. Thus, in our attempt to understand human nature we cannot fail to be much interested in scrutinizing the structure of the catastrophic condition in our patients and in learning how the abnormal person overcomes it.

To begin with their structure, one might argue that ordered and catastrophic behavior represent the reactions of the individual to good and bad performances. Such an assumption, however, fails to accord with the observation that the patient is very often unable to tell why he is restless, angry, afraid, negativistic, and so on. Frequently — usually, in fact — he does not realize that the cause of his anxiety was a specific task which was demanded of him and to which he was not equal. We have already pointed out that our patients are especially disturbed in the capacity for giving themselves an account of what they are doing. Therefore we must be allowed to assume that they are unable to give themselves an account of the difficulty of the task required, of their failure, of the consequences which this failure may have, etc. Thus we may say that catastrophic behavior is not simply a consequence of lacking the capacity to perform but rather belongs to the situation of failing. The same is true in the case of ordered behavior. It belongs to the situation of doing well.

In order to make this clear we shall supplement our explanations by further comments on the functioning of the nervous system.

We have already discussed the conditions under which the organism functions in a constant and ordered way. We stressed especially the significance of the equalization process, which brings the organism back to its average state of excitation.* What

* See p. 15.

we call a normal performance or an appropriate reaction to a definite stimulus corresponds to an excitation pattern within this average zone of excitability. The maintenance of constancy in the actions of an organism depends on two conditions: (1) that the organism be normal, and (2) that the external stimuli do not differ too strongly from the adequate stimuli, those suited to the organism concerned.

What do we mean by the phrase "adequate stimuli"? [3] We know the organism does not react to all stimuli in the same way. There are many events to which a particular organism is not sensitive. I need not mention the fact that every organism, including the human organism, is insensitive to stimuli to which other organisms react. Each has its special organization as to sensory equipment, etc., and usually is responsive only to stimuli relevant to this, its "nature." As we shall see later, it is the basic tendency of the organism to actualize itself in accordance with its nature. All performances that can be observed are expressions of the activity of the organism in this direction. This actualization means existence, life. Normally the organism responds only to those stimuli which are "adequate" — that is, relevant — to its nature. Normal equalization is possible, and the organism is in a state of ordered behavior, only so long as it is not affected by inadequate stimuli; and only in this ordered state is it able to carry on the performances that correspond to its nature.

Therefore to live in a milieu which allows for ordered behavior, which allows especially for normal equalization, is requisite for the organism's living at all. The proper milieu of the organism is not the entire environment but only that part with which it can come to terms in such a way that normal equalization is possible. Each organism has its own characteristic milieu. Only that, a certain segment of all that surrounds it, constitutes its world. We call this milieu the adequate milieu, that is, the milieu that is appropriate to the nature of the organism.[4] Contact with it does not alter the organism in such a way that it becomes unable to realize its own nature. The stimuli arising from it we call adequate stimuli.

The very existence of the organism is tied up with the possibility of finding an adequate milieu within its environment. Normally, the adaptation of the organism to its environment — that is, congruency between the two — is developed to such a degree that existence is guaranteed.

The organism ordinarily does not react at all to stimuli which are inadequate to it. Such stimuli can become effective only if they are very strong and force themselves upon the organism; then it is driven into the catastrophic situation, not only because it is unable to react adequately but also because it is so shocked and disturbed in its functioning that, for a longer or shorter period, it is unable to react at all. This brings it into the danger of not being able to carry on even those performances which are essential for its existence, and in this sense we may consider catastrophic behavior as a threat to the existence of the organism.

For several reasons this situation takes place more often in abnormal persons than in normal ones. Every injury to the nervous system involves an impairment of structure and an impairment of the normal reactions of the substratum and of the process of equalization. The result is that the sick organism is not able to react adequately even to normal stimuli, which become "inadequate." Catastrophic reactions consequently take place even during normal tasks, and catastrophic situations appear very easily. Furthermore, they endanger the existence of the abnormal person more than that of a normal one because his performances are so limited by his illness that he is more likely to be unable to realize essential capacities.

It may be difficult to understand how failure in such apparently unimportant tasks as, for example, simple arithmetic, can bring an individual into a state that actually endangers his existence. In order to understand it, one must bear in mind that any failure or lack of ability, which to a normal person would be merely somewhat disagreeable, may produce in the abnormal one a sense of such inadequacy that it blocks his ability to perform at all. The danger to his existence does not depend upon a special task but on the fact that the task places him in the situation of not being able to react in accordance with his essential capacities. With that, realization of the essential capacities is endangered — that is, life, existence itself.

As we have said before, the phenomenon of anxiety belongs to the catastrophic condition. That is, anxiety corresponds on the subjective side to a condition in which the organism's existence is in danger. Anxiety is *the subjective experience of that danger to existence.* The catastrophic condition and the phenomenon of anxiety, in short, have a special significance for life. We feel that we are correct in assuming that both of them are to be found in all living creatures, in animals as well as in man — that they belong to life itself.[5]

There is one point which must be stressed. We have explained that our patients are not aware of the causes of the catastrophic conditions they experience. Thus we may conclude that, subjectively, anxiety is not connected causally with the experience of an *event* in the external world. Objectively, it is true, the condition is connected with such an event. The organism, shaken by the catastrophic shock, stands in relation to a definite objective reality, and the basic phenomenon of anxiety, the occurrence of disordered behavior, is understandable only in terms of this relation. The subject, however, is not aware of this objective reality; he experiences only the shock, only anxiety. His anxiety is the result of the disordered functioning of his organism, not a reaction to an object. And what holds true for the patient's anxiety holds true for anxiety in general. Our observations of many patients confirm the interpretation offered by most philosophers and psychologists who have dealt with anxiety, that it represents an emotional state which does not refer to anything definite, that the source of anxiety is nothing and nowhere. Anxiety deals with nothingness. It is the inner experience of being faced with nothingness.

This statement is correct only if one distinguishes strictly between anxiety and another emotional state which is very often confused with it — fear. Superficially, fear may have many of the characteristics of anxiety, but intrinsically it is different. The student of human nature has every reason to distinguish sharply between these two phenomena. They are not characteristic of man in the same way. Anxiety, as we have said, belongs to the life of all organisms; fear, however, seems to be confined to the "higher" organisms, perhaps only to man, because, as we shall see, it presupposes the abstract attitude.

Let us call attention to some phenomenological differences between anxiety and fear. In the state of fear we have an object before us that we can meet, that we can attempt to remove, or from which we can flee. We are conscious of ourselves as well as of the object; we can deliberate as to how we shall behave toward it, and we can look at the cause of the fear, which actually lies before us. Anxiety, on the other hand, gets at us from the back, so to speak. The only thing we can do is to attempt to flee from it, but without knowing what direction to take, because we experience it as coming from no particular place. This flight is sometimes successful, merely by chance, but usually it fails and anxiety remains with us. The assumption that we are dealing with qualitative differences is supported by the fact that we have two different words, "fear" and "anxiety," and that these words are not interchangeable. In German the distinction between them is more definite than in English; it is reflected in such expressions as "Ich fürchte *etwas*" and "Ich ängstige *mich*." We shall use *fear* as corresponding to the German word *Furcht* and *anxiety* as corresponding to *Angst*.

We have said that anxiety corresponds to the experience of danger to existence. What is characteristic of the object of fear? Is it something inherent in the object itself, at all times? Of course not. An object that at one time arouses only interest, or is met with indifference, at another time may evoke the greatest fear. In other words, what results in fear must be something which is found only in a specific relationship between organism and object. What is it, then, that leads to fear? Nothing but the experience of the possibility of the onset of anxiety. What we fear is the *impending* anxiety. Thus it becomes clear that anxiety cannot be derived from the phenomenon of fear, and that only the opposite procedure is logical. The person who is afraid knows anxiety from past experience as well as through imagination and anticipation. The person in a state of anxiety, however, cannot know fear, because in the state of anxiety he is incapable of any recollection of the past.

Because the person in a state of fear is not yet in a state of anxiety, but only envisions it, because he only fears that anxiety may befall him, he is not so disturbed in his judgment of the outer world as the person in a state of anxiety. On the contrary, driven by the tendency to get rid of the fear, he attempts to establish special contact with the outer world. He tries to recognize the situation as clearly as possible, and to react to it in an appropriate manner, in order to free himself, either by attack or flight, from the impending anxiety-situation. Fear is conditioned by, and directed against, very definite aspects of the environment. These have to be recognized and, if possible, removed. Fear sharpens the senses, whereas anxiety renders them unusable; fear drives to action, anxiety paralyzes. We can escape anxiety only by avoiding situations which might result in anxiety.

From these explanations it is obvious that to feel anxiety it is not necessary to be able to give oneself an account of one's acts; to feel fear, however, presupposes that capacity. The observation of our patients teaches us that they are very much affected by anxiety but not by fear. This corresponds to the fact that their attitude toward the abstract is impaired and that they are therefore unable to look into the future. Thus it is understandable that fear should be a phenomenon especially characteristic of the normal *adult* human being. Infants, in whom the abstract attitude is still in the process of development, are much more harassed by anxiety than by fear.

Now how does the abnormal person get rid of his catastrophic reaction and, with it, of anxiety?

We have stressed the fact that catastrophic situations are especially dangerous for the sick man. The tendency to avoid them therefore is a dominant feature of his whole behavior. Avoiding catastrophic situations is possible only if he is able to come to terms with the world in spite of his defects — that is, only if he finds a new milieu which is appropriate to his defective condition, a milieu from which no stimuli arise which put him into a catastrophic condition. As I have said before, sooner or later after the injury to the brain, catastrophic reactions become rarer, and the patient grows quiet, happier, and more friendly.

I have had an opportunity to observe this change of behavior in great detail in many patients, since during and after the war of 1914 I was in charge of a large hospital for soldiers with brain injuries. These injured men remained for many years and lived under conditions that in a way were well adapted to the mental changes that had occurred in them. Two or three lived together in a room which they had to keep very tidy. Each had his own things, his own wardrobe, and so on. During the time the men were in the hospital they collected many articles, which they stored in their wardrobes. The life of these patients was ordered in general by household regulations. Mealtimes were definitely fixed, as were times for walking, resting during the day, going to bed at night, and so on. The patients had an opportunity to go to concerts, motion pictures, and theaters, and to have visitors, and there were many other forms of recreation. Within this general framework of regulation, however, they still had many opportunities to arrange their lives in a strictly individual manner.

Now how did the patient, under these conditions, avoid catastrophic situations and find a milieu adequate to his defect? One way to escape catastrophe consists in voluntarily withdrawing, to a greater or less degree, from the world. In extreme cases the only way out is through loss of consciousness, a factor which plays an important role in the disturbance of consciousness appearing in epileptics. One of my patients, living in an adequate milieu, as in the hospital, was usually quiet and well-behaved. This state lasted as long as he had to do only those tasks to which he was equal. When faced with a task to which he was not equal, he began to tremble violently, showed signs of catastrophic behavior, and often fell into unconsciousness for a short time. In his case a catastrophic reaction of the severest type, leading to unconsciousness, could be produced experimentally. If, after the patient had returned to his normal condition, he was asked what had been the matter with him and what had been demanded of him, he could give no information whatever.

Resorting to unconsciousness is, of course, hardly a suitable means of avoiding catastrophic situations, since it totally abolishes contact between the patient and his environment. The organism, therefore, commonly seeks protection in another way — namely, by avoiding particularly dangerous situations and by seeking other situations which promise a minimum of irritating stimuli. In discussing this avoidance of situations, we must bear in mind that the mentally sick cannot achieve such a thing by conscious effort; our patients, as we have seen, were unable to recognize whether or not a situation was dangerous for them, because they were impaired in the capacity which makes this judgment possible. Avoidance takes place in a rather passive way. If the patient has had some experience of being disturbed in a catastrophic way in certain situations, and if he is able to recognize these situations by certain particulars, then, warned by such criteria, he may withdraw from the dangerous approach. In such cases he does not recognize the real cause of the danger but is influenced by some warning signal. We often observe that patients persistently resist certain tasks which, to us, seem entirely harmless. We can understand the behavior of the patient in these cases only when we see the situation from the point of view of the danger it presents to that patient.

Another method of escaping danger is found in

not reacting at all to the required task. If the examiner urges the patient, he often gives an answer which is not correct but by which he can escape the situation — for example, "I don't know"; "That does not interest me"; "I don't like it." Usually the patient gives these answers very quickly, with a much quicker reaction than in other situations. One gets the impression that he has a great desire to hurry out of a dangerous situation. His countenance shows a mixture of anxiety and embarrassment, though he may be smiling and seem full of determination. Through these expressions he covers his uncertainty, hiding it from the examiner and probably from himself as well. You will understand the condition of the patient if you imagine yourself taking part in an important examination. You are unable to answer an important question; you feel the same embarrassment, the same desire to cover up the situation by evasion and excuses, by giving an answer or doing anything which you know is right in itself, although it does not fit this particular instance, for in so doing you hope to draw the examiner away from the point at issue. In such a situation you need not be any more conscious of what you are doing than the patient. Both of you act as if driven by the desire to get away from a dangerous situation, and you use the same means of doing so.

It is natural that the patient should seek protection by avoiding company and situations out of which troublesome demands may arise. But this does not

mean that he is not in contact with his environment
and that he is doing nothing. On the contrary, he is
always busy at something — not by accident but because this activity protects him from disturbances
which may arise. He avoids a catastrophic situation
indirectly *by busying himself with those things which
he is able to do.* No stimulus is so dangerous for him
as an unexpected one, because the quick readjustment which the reaction demands is very difficult for
him, and may even be impossible. We observe again
and again that patients start violently when suddenly
addressed. It is not necessary that what is said be
irritating in itself. What acts as the irritant is the
mere fact that the stimulus comes from a situation
not belonging to the patient's immediate milieu and
therefore demands a particular adjustment which he
cannot make. Very often he does not react at all to
such stimuli, and this has been explained as inatten-
tion. If spoken to with greater vehemence, however,
he will respond. By keeping busy he is aided in his
desire to avoid these sudden irritations. The activities which engross him need not be of great value in
themselves; their usefulness consists in their protective character. We call them "substitute reactions." Just what performances appear as substitute
reactions depends on the individuality of the patient
and upon the particular conditions of the environment. Wherever we find such performances we have
to remember that the patient is in a condition in
which he is afraid of catastrophic situations. The

value of these substitute reactions is not primary but secondary.

These phenomena have received much attention in neurotics, but it must be noted that organic cases behave in the same way. These phenomena in both cases have the same character and the same origin functionally, differing only in their etiology. When produced organically, the defect in special performances that results in the danger of entering a catastrophic situation comes from the organic defect of the patient and his inability to fulfill the demands of his environment; in the neurotic it is due to the fact that he is incapable of mastering the battle in his own soul.

This flight from demands with which they cannot cope makes it plain that our patients are incapable of the contemplative attitude of normal persons, that they cannot take themselves for granted and play the role of detached spectators. For the same reason our patients will not walk merely for the sake of walking, without a definite goal. They may be able to find a known path easily, but they go for a walk only if they have a special purpose — for example, if they are going somewhere in particular or want to fetch something. They do not stroll about, for strolling about contains in it many dangers of abrupt stimulation. Thus the patient avoids it, and may even resist going to a known goal by an unfamiliar route, even if accompanied by a friend. He tries at all costs to avoid the unknown.

Another protection from catastrophic situations is excessive and fanatical orderliness. Suppose, in sitting and talking with a patient, you put several objects at random on a table. If he becomes aware of them, he will at once arrange them in some order. Or, to take another example, a patient has just written something for me on a sheet of paper. The examination is concluded. "That is all," I say, make a quick note, and drop the pencil on the sheet of paper, which happens to be lying aslant. The patient takes up the pencil, straightens the paper carefully so as to bring its sides parallel with the side of the table, and then as carefully places the pencil parallel to the margin of the paper. I change the pencil to an oblique position, and the patient once more puts it back into the parallel position. This game can be kept up for some time. If the patient is made to desist, being told that the pencil is to be left in the oblique position, he will obey, but with visible signs of discomfort. Apparently such a state of "disorder" is unbearable to him. Similar tendencies can be observed in regard to time, in behaving in accordance with instructions and in response to household regulations, in thinking, and in behavior in general. The patients fulfill required tasks meticulously, and become unhappy, even excited, if they are interrupted by anyone in their work before it is finished. They are punctual in their daily activities, in bathing, going to bed, etc., doing everything at the prescribed time. I have already said that the patients under my observation were supposed to look after their personal belongings. Nothing was more illuminating to me than the wardrobes and closets of these people and the extreme care with which innumerable odds and ends, the accumulation of ten years' residence, were always arranged. Everything had its appointed place; and not only that — it had to occupy that place in a definite way. Looking more closely, one discovered a utilitarian motive behind this formal geometry — namely, that of bringing each article within the patient's reach with a minimum of effort on his part.

It may prove interesting to stop a moment here and consider what is meant by the words "order" and "disorder." It is impossible to characterize a distribution of objects once and for all as either orderly or disorderly. Total disorder would be a completely haphazard distribution, as far as such an arrangement is possible. Further, what may appear to one person as order may be disorder for another, depending on the attitude of each and the capacity of each to change his attitude. The adequate distribution of certain objects may be one thing for the contemplative individual and quite another for a person whose approach is behavioral. A person with a behavioral approach would find a distribution orderly which enabled him to use the objects as easily and as quickly as possible in the situation in which he was acting. Furthermore, the distribution might vary greatly with different tasks. A distribution which is adequate for a simple action may be inadequate for a complex one and may even hinder the person who has to use the same objects in different combinations and in different situations. The distribution of the objects on the desk of a very busy man may seem disorderly if you have no insight into the purposes for which they are to be used. When you have this insight, you see that it may be the best order it is possible to find in the situation. It is not uncommon for housewives or maids to feel an irresistible desire to put such objects in "good" order, to the dismay of the man to whom the desk belongs.

For a person who is capable of using objects only for very simple actions that arrangement will be best which makes it possible for him to grasp each thing easily when he needs it. That means an arrangement of objects one beside the other in a place where each can be taken hold of quickly. This arrangement is "order" for such a person, all other arrangements "disorder."

This primitive type of order is adequate for the man with a severe brain injury, since it makes it possible for him to perform such simple actions as he is capable of. Any change puts him into a state of the greatest excitement. For example, one day the patients of my hospital had to be moved from one ward to another. One of our patients had intended to go to his relatives for some weeks during this time, a thing he very much liked to do. But when he learned that moving would take place while he was

away, he refrained from making the visit. He did
not wish to abandon his possessions — not that he
thought anyone would steal them; he was simply
afraid that they would be disarranged and left in a
condition that would make it difficult for him to find
them. In any other arrangement he would have to
decide which object to use in a given situation, and
that was particularly difficult for him, at times even
impossible. The anxiety that arises out of a situation in which he is unable to function leads to his
holding with great pertinacity to a simple, primitive
arrangement. It is adequate for him, however, and
enables him to get along in an undisturbed fashion.
The sense of order in the patient is thus an expression
of some pathology, an expression of the impairment
of an essential faculty of human beings, the faculty
of meaningfully changing their behavior.

Not all our patients are orderly to the degree we
have described, however. Sometimes we find patients
who exhibit the contrary behavior. This is particularly the case when they are in an acute condition of
change, in excitation, in depression, and so on. But
in these states of disease they are very often shocked
by catastrophic situations. In chronic disease, where
there is a quieter general condition, we find this
abnormal orderliness as a concomitant factor.

One may observe in the behavior of these patients
another phenomenon, which one might describe as
abhorrence of a vacuum, a *horror vacui*. If the
patient is faced objectively either with a vacuum in

space or with a situation which contains no possibility for him of reaction, he immediately becomes troubled, anxious. For example, a patient is asked to write a letter, or just his name, on an empty sheet of paper. We observe that he hesitates and seems embarrassed. He does not know where he ought to write, and so he writes at the very top of the paper, very often parallel to the top edge. Asked to write something more, to write to dictation, he joins the new words closely to the first ones written. If you try to induce him to write in the middle of the sheet, he begins to object and becomes excited. Very often it is impossible to get him to write there. But he will do so instantly if you draw a line upon which he can write. At first it may seem that the patient is unable to write without a line, but further examination shows that this is not the cause of his deficiency; if it were, he would not have been able to write without a line at the top of the sheet. No, the deficiency does not consist in an incapacity for writing without lines but in the inability to do anything without clinging to a given concrete object. This inability induces the patient to write near the top edge of the paper or — and this is very amazing — if he is not allowed to do that, to draw a line at another place on the sheet parallel to the edge and to write below that, always looking at it as he writes. Even more striking is another example: a patient was unable to read letters or words if they were not written on a line. If you wrote a letter on the blackboard without a line, he took the chalk, drew a line under it, and immediately could read it.

There is no question but that our patients try to avoid the situation of emptiness. But we cannot assume that they behave so because of having the *experience* of emptiness. For having that experience certainly demands what we have called an abstract attitude, in which our patients, as we know, are lacking. This abhorrence of a vacuum is caused by the fact that empty space is not an adequate stimulus. The patient cannot handle it, and from this incapacity arises the catastrophic situation. Faced with this condition, the patient recognizes that he is unable to act and tries to evade the difficulty by clinging to an object which he can cope with.

Now we must discuss further a very interesting and important means by which our patients are protected against catastrophic situations, namely, the means by which dangerous stimuli arising from the defect itself, and from the impending realization of the defect by the patient, are excluded.

It is an amazing but very characteristic fact that people with brain diseases are very often totally unconscious of their deviation from the normal, of the difference between their own state prior to the development of the disease and after it. Their unawareness is strikingly displayed when they speak to the physician of their troubles. It is astonishing how very small a part is played in their complaints by the paralysis of a leg or the hemianopic defect, by disturbances of speech, of recognition, of manipulation, etc. This becomes exceedingly impressive when the existing defect tends toward a totality, such as complete blindness, complete loss of speech. It is important to notice, however, that what happens here is not simply that the patient is subjectively unaware of his defects but that objectively he has so compensated in his attitude and actions that they cause very little difficulty in the field which they concern. The analysis of this process of adjustment leads us to stress the fact that the adjustment is made in proportion to the severity of the defect. When the latter completely blocks any essential activity, the readjustment becomes much better than in cases of lesser disturbances. When, for example, sight is entirely gone, the patient compensates far more thoroughly than when his vision is merely impaired.

I once had a patient who had been shot through the optic nerve (*chiasma opticum*) and was at first totally blind. As long as this lasted he was not conscious of being blind. He used to talk of visual things like any seeing person; he was quiet, his behavior was orderly, and one could see that he managed to get along with the help of his other senses and that he adjusted without difficulty in the hospital environment. Later his injury improved and to a certain degree he regained his sight. Then he became upset; he sought to orient himself by means of sight but, owing to its imperfection, succeeded badly. He was thus less well adapted to his world than when he had been blind. Now, for the first time, he spoke of something's not being right with his vision, and this previously quite reasonably contented man dropped into a state of depression. "What's to become of me if I can't see?" he would cry.

From this and similar experiences we may conclude that alterations are shut out from the life of the organism when they would seriously impair any of its essential functions. If total blindness remained permanently present to the patient's consciousness and his situation were the impossible one of facing visual demands which he could never meet, then the only possible procedure would be the catastrophic reaction. But the organism so threatened spontaneously reaches a new equilibrium through readjustment to the non-visual world.

We observe all these ways of escaping catastrophic situations not only in cases of major brain defects but also in severe bodily disease. Most people have heard about the characteristic euphoria in patients in the last stage of tuberculosis. (I might recall here the masterly description of this condition in Thomas Mann's novel, *The Magic Mountain*.) In this we meet with a very general biological phenomenon: what seems to be a kindness on the part of nature saves the organism from an experience too poignant to be borne.

Using what we have learned by studying patients with brain defects, we are ready to discuss the role which anxiety and fear play in normal human life. In normal life, unquestionably, incongruities often arise between the capacities of the organism and the tasks imposed by constellations of stimuli in the environment; for example, an organism may have to cope continually with new tasks — i.e., with tasks which contain factors not in keeping with the condition of the organism. The conquest of the world inevitably forces the organism over and over into such situations. Consequently we assume that the "coming to terms" with the world must proceed by way of constantly recurring catastrophic situations, with concomitant emotions of the character of anxiety. This is actually the case. To be sure, anxiety in its full strength does not always appear when one is incapable of solving a problem. It occurs only when the situation is of a particular kind. In patients with brain injuries it is induced by the fact that the impossibility of solving any given problem acts very easily as a menace to the existence of the individual. In normal persons such a situation — i.e., not being able to solve a given problem — usually does not really put the individual into such danger. The normal person has many possibilities for managing the situation without threat to his existence. And here the abstract attitude plays a very great role. Thus real anxiety does not always appear, but the structure of the emotion is of the same kind, though slighter in degree. This emotional reaction may increase to real anxiety in a moment, however, if an event in itself apparently unimportant takes place in a situation in which it can become dangerous. For example, in an examination that is very important real anxiety may appear very quickly.

As might be expected, the appearance of anxiety is to be observed especially in the child, who is definitely not yet adapted to his environment. Staring, the expression of astonishment, a condition surely closely related to anxiety, is characteristic of the child. But the urge for activity is so great in the child that he does not shrink back from the danger of anxiety situations; indeed, he even seeks them. There is a German tale for children, about how Little John went out into the world to learn to shudder, which tells how a little boy is driven by the desire to learn to know the dreads and dangers of the world. The story brings home very well the characteristic behavior of children. Again and again we see that children not only do not avoid dangers but actually seek them out as something to be coped with. In place of an anxious astonishment there develops surprise touched with satisfaction at having mastered a bit of the world. Thus anxiety is overcome by activity in the sense of a fruitful coming to terms with the world, not, as in our patients, by the avoidance of reality and the building up of a world which is a shelter from the dangers of reality.

As the child becomes adapted to the world of the adult, its behavior becomes more even and ordered;

its personality becomes more balanced and settled;
its "wondering" decreases. Yet this wondering never
disappears completely, and the adult, too, again and
again is shaken by astonishment and anxiety whenever he finds himself facing new outer and inner
situations and problems which he cannot solve. Like
the person with a brain injury, though to a much
smaller degree, the normal person has the urge to
diminish his anxiety. As an expression of it, we
find the tendency toward order, norms, continuity,
and homogeneity, similar in principle to the tendency
exhibited by our patients. But, on the other hand,
the normal person is also driven by his inherent
desire for new experiences, for the conquest of the
world, and for an expansion of the sphere of his
activity in a practical and spiritual sense. His behavior oscillates between these two tendencies, and
is influenced now by one, now by the other. The
outcome of the interaction of the two is the development of culture and the products of culture. But one
can in no way maintain that the ordered world
which culture represents is the product of anxiety,
the result of the desire to avoid anxiety. Freud,
for example, conceives of culture as a sublimation
of repressed drives. This is a complete misappre-
hension of the creative trend of human nature, and
at the same time leaves one question completely
unanswered: why the cultural world should have
taken shape in certain patterns, and why just these
forms should be suited to win security for man. The

matter becomes intelligible only if one regards the forms as expressions of the creative power of man, and of his tendency to effect a realization of his nature. Only when the world is adequate to man's nature do we find what we call security.

This tendency toward actualization is primary, but it can achieve its end only through a conflict with the opposing forces of the environment. This never happens without shock and anxiety. Thus we are probably not overstating the facts if we maintain that these shocks are essential to human nature and if we conclude that life must, of necessity, take its course via uncertainty and shock.

Whenever anxiety, as the mainspring of the activity of an organism, comes into the foreground, we find that something is awry in the nature of that organism. To put it conversely, an organism is normal and healthy when its tendency toward self-actualization issues from within, and when it overcomes the disturbance arising from its clash with the world not by virtue of anxiety but through the joy of coming to terms with the world. How often this perfect form of actualization occurs, we leave open to question. In any event, even life in its most nearly perfect manifestation must go through the disturbances which emerge from the adjustment to the environment. The creative person, who ventures into many situations which expose him to shock, gets into these anxiety situations more often and more readily than the average person. The more original a human being is, the deeper his anxiety is, said Søren Kierkegaard. According to this philosopher, the cause of not being able to come to terms with the world, the cause of anxiety, is the inability to come to terms with the phenomenon of sin. The more original a human being is, the more he experiences this inability — and with it, anxiety.

Individuals differ as to how much anxiety they can bear. For a patient with a brain injury, the amount is very low; for a child it is greater; and for the creative individual it is still greater. The capacity for bearing anxiety is the manifestation of genuine courage, in which ultimately one is concerned not with the things of the world but with a threat to existence. *In the final analysis courage is nothing but an affirmative answer to the shocks of existence, to the shocks which it is necessary to bear for the sake of realizing one's own nature.* This form of overcoming anxiety requires the ability to view a single experience within a larger context, i.e., to assume the "attitude toward the possible," to maintain freedom of decision regarding different possibilities. This attitude is peculiar to man, and it is because persons with brain injuries have lost it, and have suffered a consequent impairment of freedom, that they are so completely helpless when facing an anxiety situation. They surrender entirely to the anxiety situation, unless they are safeguarded against it through a limitation of their world which reduces their existence to the simplest forms.

The manner in which creatures in general, and human beings in particular, cope with anxiety provides insight into their nature. Nothing shows more clearly the connection between freedom and the capacity for sustaining anxiety, and makes it so evident that freedom is inherent in human nature, than the difference between the behavior of a person with a brain injury and a normal personality. The more the normal person is able to bear of pain and grief — pain and grief from which no human being is safe, as I believe, because of the phenomenon of individualization — the more surely he preserves his freedom.

When normal people are beset to an abnormal degree by anxiety, they are unable to actualize themselves, and the result is catastrophic situations, with their consequences. Abnormal states of anxiety grow out of various causes, but fundamentally they result from the fact that the individual is in a state of uncertainty about his existence, taking this term in its broadest meaning. This uncertainty may be based upon external or internal difficulties; it may rest upon events in the personal life of the individual or upon the condition of a group, a class, a people, a nation, and so on.

Uncertainty and anxiety force the individual into abnormal activities (i.e., substitute phenomena) or into neurosis or suicide. Substitute phenomena reveal their abnormal character, their origin in the abnormal isolation produced by anxiety, by their abnormal stress on *partial* aspects of human action or nature, and by their compulsiveness, their lack of freedom and relationship to reality, to life. Their true nature is sometimes misunderstood because they may have a high value in themselves, as, for example, when they consist in religious beliefs, in valuable scientific ideas, in sacrificing oneself for political reasons. However, as long as these activities are not spontaneous, are not outlets for the free personality, but are merely the sequelae of anxiety, they have only a pseudo value for the personality. They always mean a shrinkage of the freedom of one's world. This can be well illustrated by the difference between the sincere faith of the really religious man, which is based upon willing devotion to the infinite, and superstitious beliefs. Or by the difference between the open-minded scholar who bases his belief upon facts and is always ready to change his conceptions when faced with new facts, and the dogmatic scientist, who maintains his ideas in an obstinate way and supports them by far-fetched auxiliary hypotheses because he fears the crash of his artificially maintained structure — a type to be found in any period. There is a saying attributed to the Chinese philosopher Chuang-tse which shows that four hundred years before Christ there was no difference in this respect. Chuang-tse said: With a learned person it is impossible to discuss the problems of life; he is bound by his system.

If the shrinkage of personal life reaches too high

a degree and nature does not help the individual by blinding him to the danger to existence which this state involves, then courage reaches its limit. The person involved may then fall into insanity, as very often happened in the horrible situations of the first World War. Or he may become conscious of the conflict within him and turn to suicide as the only means of protecting himself from the perpetual fear of catastrophic situations and the terrible experience of not being able to carry out tasks which appear to him as the essence of life. A deliberate decision to commit suicide presupposes that the individual gives an account of the situation to himself and willingly chooses death as the ultimate solution. Suicide, therefore, is a phenomenon we observe only in man. No animal commits suicide. Neither do patients with brain injuries, except in states of transition in which they are aware of their situation. With them, suicide — at least, the kind of suicide we have in mind — is a very rare phenomenon, and the same is the case with animals. An animal which is in great anxiety or a patient who is in the same situation or who is suffering to an extreme degree may react to this situation in such a way that he hurts himself and dies, as a man running amok runs into death. Here, however, we are not dealing with an action of the will but with a sequence of disorder and confusion belonging to the catastrophic situation, in which the actions of the individual inadvertently cause death. Death then is a mere accident; it is not desired by the individual and should not be called suicide. Suicide is a voluntary act, and, with that, a phenomenon belonging to abstract behavior and thus characteristic of human nature alone.

When anxiety besets groups or nations, it may force individuals into very strange situations and lead them to renounce reason and freedom to a degree that seems unbelievable to the objective observer. This is especially the case in the political field. Shaken on the one hand by uneasiness about the present situation and by anxiety for their existence, deceived on the other by the mockery of a brilliant future as the political demagogue depicts it, a people may give up freedom and accept subordination or virtual slavery. And it may do this in the hope of getting rid of anxiety. This is the condition which tyrants of any kind utilize for subduing free people, for transforming them from people into masses. The characteristic difference between free people and masses consists in the fact that the former determine themselves in liberty, bear pain and distress, but do this, conscious of necessity, with a free will, with courage. Thus, in spite of all necessary restrictions, they remain individuals, human beings. The man in the masses is not free and does not think about what he is doing; yet he may be happy in not needing to think. He does not need courage; he finds protection against his anxiety in the will of other individuals. He behaves like a

man with an injured brain; he lacks the highest
capacity of human nature, the attitude toward the
abstract, losing himself in activities determined by
concrete demands. Therefore he lacks true community with his fellow men, for true community
presupposes freedom in action and freedom to
renounce one's right as an individual for the sake
of one's fellow men. Masses are made up of passive
beings, driven together by equal needs and equal
anxiety. And as the attitude of one of our patients
can easily be modified by a skillful person who knows
his needs and his fears, so the attitude of the man in
the masses can be changed, and he can be induced
to fight even against people who shortly before had
been his closest friends. The more firmly their community is based on the freedom of the individual —
that is, the more truly democratic it is — the more
individual men will resist such influences.

The differences between individuals in a true
community and those in masses governed by a
dictator of any kind lead back ultimately to
differences in the capacity for taking the abstract
attitude. There is no better means, therefore, of
enslaving people and destroying democracy than to
weaken this capacity. And there is no better means
of attaining that goal than to create in people a
state of anxiety. One of the basic pillars of all kinds
of fascism, consequently, is anxiety.

Subjugation to a tyrannical government is then the
last refuge from suicide. Instead of physical death,

the individual chooses a more or less conscious form of suicide with respect to the essence of human nature. How near it is to real suicide can be learned from the fact that in such political situations physical suicide is a very frequent event in the camp of the political party in power as well as in that of its opponents. The individual is always in a state of conflict between physical suicide and the renunciation of what is to him the essence of human nature. States of anxiety in groups have the characteristics we have described in individuals, and many phenomena of social life — revolutions and wars, especially the latter — are understandable only in these terms.

From what we have said, it is plain that we can understand the behavior of an organism, and so also of a human being, only if we take into account the mechanisms used to avoid catastrophic situations. In pathological cases the tendency to avoid catastrophies is very prominent; yet even here the individual is not governed by this tendency alone, for he tries to make use of his capacities. This is even more strongly the case in normal people. An understanding of normal behavior, consequently, asks especially for knowledge of the capacities that are characteristic of a particular individual.

V

COMING TO TERMS WITH THE WORLD

Now WHAT are the means of determining the capacities of the individual? Observation under the atomistic method reveals a great variety of phenomena. Among them we can distinguish phenomena that are directly observable and phenomena that can be determined only indirectly, through the communication of the individual's inner experiences. Thus we observe motor actions of various kinds, habits, various sensory experiences, moods, feelings, thoughts, motives, tendencies, needs, desires, drives, etc. Aside from these innumerable phenomena revealed by analytic examination, the organism, especially the human organism, appears to us as a *unit* of which these manifold phenomena are the manifestations. But this is a mere pre-scientific impression. Ours is the task of construing this unity on the basis of the phenomena we observe. Such an endeavor to construe the whole, however, meets at the very outset the skeptical opposition that it is not necessary to assume such a unit to explain the behavior of an organism, that the observable phenomena are to be understood without reference to a personality unit. Personality, according to this theory, is nothing more than a collection of hundreds or thousands of independent specific habits which may be determined statistically.[1] They originate in certain inborn stimulus-response patterns or in the functioning of definite anatomic and physiological apparatuses. Upon these inborn reactions, acquired reactions are built up as conditioned reflexes.

We cannot speak here of the lack of a real anatomical basis for this theory. Such famous investigators as Coghill, Herrick, Lashley, Bethe, and others, are not at all inclined to admit the existence of such anatomical mechanisms.[2] In several investigations made many years ago I myself tried to demonstrate the untenability of this assumption. Often the student is not aware of the extremely speculative character of the anatomical basis of this theory. But here we must confine ourselves to a discussion of the theory itself. According to it, the reflex is supposed to be a constant reaction to a definite stimulus, and the behavior of an organism is understandable in terms of such constant responses and their combinations.[3]

Now observation of human beings shows that under natural conditions such constant reactions are very rare, if they occur at all. What we observe is a variety of reactions to the same stimulus, as well as equal or similar reactions to various stimuli. If we want a constant reaction to a stimulus, we must isolate both the stimulus and that part of the organism where the stimulus acts. If, for example, we elicit the knee jerk, the rest of the organism must be held in a definite state. The attention of the individual must be artificially diverted from the event. Only if that succeeds do we regularly get the same effect from stimulation of the tendon of the knee. The same is the case with the reflex usually considered as the prototype of reflexes: the light reflex of the pupil of the eye. A constant reaction — corresponding quantitatively to the amount of light — is to be achieved only under fixed conditions. Usually the reaction varies throughout, depending upon the differences in the mental and bodily condition of the entire organism.

Any change in any part of the organism changes every reflex reaction more or less. The reflex is apparently dependent not only upon the stimulus and upon that part of the organism where the reaction takes place but also upon the condition of the rest of the organism. A very great number of observations shows that relative constancy is reached only if the influence of all other stimuli except the reflex stimulus is experimentally hindered. This is very often overlooked, as is also the fact that during the course of a reflex the rest of the organism is also changed in a definite way. Only to superficial observation does the stimulus of the sole seem to evoke flexion of the foot alone (the so-called foot reflex) and stimulation by light the contraction of the pupils alone. The same thing is observable in many other phenomena — for example, those of muscle tone. And all these phenomena —

those representing the reflex reaction and those in other parts of the organism — are not only concomitant but constitute a unit, no part of which can be changed without changing the other parts, including the reflex reaction. This is very often overlooked because part of the organism which is considered as unrelated to the reflex reaction is artificially held constant. On the basis of observation we have to say that constant reactions in one part of the organism are phenomena corresponding to an artificial maintenance of a constant condition of the rest of the organism. They are thus in effect reactions of the whole organism, where by artificial, experimental means the reactions in the rest of the organism are held in a definite, constant state.

There do not exist discrete, individual reactions of parts, as combinations of which the behavior of the organism can be understood. On the contrary, only knowledge of the whole organism leads us to understand the various reactions we observe in isolated parts. The response to a special stimulus depends upon the significance of that stimulus for the performance required of the whole organism at the moment of stimulation and is intelligible only from this point of view.

I should like to demonstrate this by an example. The tendon reflex is usually considered as the contraction of a muscle as the result of the stimulation of its tendon. Very careful investigations by a physiologist, Hoffmann, have shown that the tendon reflexes are not elicited by the stimulation of the tendon but by the tension of the muscle which is produced by the striking of the tendon. Hoffmann therefore called these reflexes "proprioceptive" reflexes (*Eigenreflexe*), reactions to stimuli arising through the processes in the functioning of the stimulated apparatus itself.[4] The reflex action takes place in the following way. The muscle is stretched abnormally by the stroke. This tension is followed by a reflexively produced innervation by which the muscle is brought back to the average state of tension of the muscle. This is the activity of the tendon reflex. The reader will remember that to the change produced by a stimulus belongs the process of equalization by which the state of excitation is brought back to the "average" condition which makes possible the best performance. Here it makes possible the exact innervation of the muscle. The correct innervation corresponds to a definite average tone of the muscle.

The average state of tension of the single muscle is not determined by the condition of the muscle alone but by the situation of the whole organism. This might be demonstrated in the following way. If you jump down a steep incline in such a way that you always touch the ground first with your heel, then the muscles located on the anterior part of the lower segment of the leg and the quadriceps are first passively stretched and then contracted reflexively. This very sensible reaction seems to take place without any voluntary innervation and to be the consequence of a reflex process. It seems to happen without any relation to the organism as a whole. But, correct and plausible as such an explanation seems to be, it is not really so. This is to be seen by the fact that, under other conditions of the whole organism, we observe a totally different phenomenon during the same kind of abnormal tension of these muscles. If, as one walks, let us say, through a forest, one's foot sticks fast behind an object, say a stone, the muscles we mentioned before are stretched. They do not contract, however, in response to that tension. On the contrary, they *relax,* and the opposite muscles — those of the back of the leg — contract, for only so can the foot be released and a fall be avoided. This reaction, too, takes place without our knowledge, without our will — which means reflexively; yet it is certainly not an innervation caused by the abnormal tension alone, but one determined rather by the condition of the organism as a whole.

Now if we assume that the change of peripheral innervation in *this* case is determined by the whole organism, we have no reason not to assume the same in the other case. Thus we obtain the following result: The reflexive reaction to a change in the periphery is determined by the condition of the whole organism. This means that so-called reflexive reactions are reactions corresponding to the condition of the whole organism.

We might also react in a voluntary way to the peripheral change, i.e., to the overtension. But this voluntary reaction would come too late, and the organism would be in danger of injury. In such situations reflex reactions take place, but, as we have seen, they are determined by the condition of the entire organism. They represent a special type of reaction of the organism as a whole. We may say then that so-called reflexive reactions appear during certain states of the organism as a whole, i.e., in situations of danger in which the organism cannot react quickly enough voluntarily. But what is most important is that they are reactions corresponding to the situation involving the organism as a whole.

Furthermore, closer experimental studies of the isolated reactions in human beings which are commonly used in support of the reflex theory reveal phenomena which speak directly against its basic assumption of the single relationship between stimulus and reaction. For example, we observe in many different parts of the body that most of these isolated reflex reactions can be reversed — i.e., the reflex reaction does not depend solely upon the specific stimulus, but, in addition, what was considered in the experiment to be stimulus apparently can be changed by what was considered to be reaction. That is, there is usually a mutual influence of the two factors. Under certain experimental conditions, for instance, we can produce a change of the position of the limbs by bringing the head into a certain position. This relationship is considered as the effect of a neck reflex from the head upon the limbs (one of the so-called Magnus-de Klejns reflexes). But the opposite is also the case. Under certain conditions we can influence the position of the head by changing the position of the limbs. On the basis of the tremendous amount of material dealing with reactions in the vegetative system, the mutual influence between certain stimuli and reactions can be demonstrated in the most impressive and convincing way. This is a very important fact which speaks against the usual idea of the reflex character of behavior.

Thus, after having reviewed all the facts in this field, one reaches the following conclusion: We are dealing with a system in which the single phenomena mutually influence one another through a circular process, which has no beginning and no end. If, starting with the observation of reflexes, we try in unbiased fashion to understand the behavior of an organism, the facts everywhere force such a point of view upon us. In this disappointing situation the adherents of the reflex theory are forced to build up supporting hypotheses by introducing factors which integrate the mechanisms of single processes and thus account for the total behavior of an organism, which is always an ordered behavior. But these regulative and integrative factors in themselves — for example, the assumed regulative higher nerve centers or a metaphysical entelechy (in Aristotle's sense) or a vitalistic principle, as Driesch [5] would call it — are all of an order totally different from the reflexes. Thus we face a situation in which one has to assume *two* essentially different determining factors in the organism: reflexes and higher regulating principles. With such a twofold assumption the essential significance of the reflex theory — its claim to explain behavior entirely on the plane of reflexes — is abandoned. But it is not merely that these adventitiously introduced factors differ in principle from the reflexes; implicitly they are usually thought of as an expression of the function of the whole organism. Consequently, the whole organism again comes into the discussion, and the very situation arises which the simple reflex theory tried to avoid.

Observations of human beings thus fail to support the stimulus-response theory; new experiments and recent critical revisions of the experiments on animals increase our skepticism regarding it.

The controversy on this issue has reached a climax during the last ten years, and more and more evidence has been adduced against the stimulus-response theory. Such investigators as John Dewey, R. S. Woodworth, Thurstone, Karl Lashley, Gordon W. Allport, Kluever, the Gestalt psychologists, Wheeler, Kantor, Warren, Carter, Jr., and others,[6] have all in various ways taken a critical stand against it. It is true that it still counts among its followers a great number of famous physiologists and psychologists. But among these many recognize the increasing difficulties which have appeared as the result not only of theoretical discussion but of the discovery of new facts and the making of innumerable new observations. Difficulties coming from the realm of fact must be taken particularly seriously, for the theory became famous chiefly because of its supposedly empirical character. More and more observations of the action of reflexes in animals have been published which appear unexplainable on the basis of the simple phenomenon of a constant connection between stimulus and reaction; more and more factors have been demonstrated to influence the reaction.

There is no paper which illustrates the situation better than the presidential address delivered before the American Psychological Association (1937) by E. C. Tolman, who without any doubt is one of the outstanding experts in this field.[7] Tolman's address deals with the simple question: What factors cause a rat in a simple T-maze to enter, at a given point of choice, one of the two channels? The task which the rat has to perform seems very easy. The animal can run in a maze of T-form from a point of choice to one of the two ends of the transverse channel, and is trained to go to one of them. The result — the dependent variable, the percentage tendency at any given state of learning for the group as a whole to turn left, the behavior ratio, as Tolman explains —

definitely does not depend upon the stimulus alone but upon many factors. It would be impossible to enumerate them all. The diagram by which Tolman illustrates the relationship between the result (the dependent variable) and the determining factors (the independent variables) is based on a very complex formula. It should be mentioned only that, in addition to the "operational factors" given in the experimental arrangement, a series of groups of factors is to be taken into consideration. These are six groups of environmental variables and four groups of individual-difference variables (heredity, age, previous training, and special endocrine, drug, or vitamin conditions). Each of these individual-difference variables is assumed to be potent to influence each of the independent variables (the operational and the environmental). Further, there are intervening variables, which have to be introduced in different ways, according to the different theories by which the reaction becomes understandable, and which are open to discussion. These intervening variables are, for example, according to Hull, "conditionings" of the running response to successive aggregates of exteroceptive, proprioceptive, and interoceptive stimuli.[8] Tolman suggests as intervening variables such factors as demand, appetite, differentiation, motor skill, hypotheses, and biases, which correspond to the various environmental variables. As far as most of these factors are concerned, an unequivocal result may be deducible from the formula which determines the reaction to a stimulus, complex as it is; the effect can be considered as a resultant of the effects of all the definable factors.

Further experiments, however, disclose one other implication which is much more detrimental to the theory. As Tolman explains, the influence of the various factors cannot be considered simply as a type of summation effect. The manner of combination of the factors does not seem to be that of simple addition. Certain factors may increase the effect of others under certain conditions, but under other circumstances they may decrease it. To this complexity, which can hardly be perceived in an unequivocal way, there finally has to be added a factor which Tolman calls "catalyzing behavior." It consists in "lookings or runnings back and forth" on the part of the animal. Kluever and Gellerman, especially, have described it in experiments with monkeys, chimpanzees, and children; according to Tolman, Muenzinger has observed the same phenomenon in rats.[9] Tolman goes so far as to suggest that "such 'lookings back and forth' might be taken as a behavioristic definition of conscious awareness." Without being able to explain it in any other way, he points to its great importance. And, indeed, he is right in doing so. This behavior apparently pertains to high mental capacities; it is decreased, for example, in rats with brain injuries. We do not know how the effect of the various factors may be modified by this phenomenon, which seems itself to be influenced by the other factors in a way not yet determinable.

This mutual influence of the factors has not received the special attention it deserves in connection with our problem. We discussed its importance when we spoke of experiments on human beings, and we saw that to take it into consideration makes it impossible to stand by the reflex theory at all. It is thus not surprising that Tolman should come to a widely negative result. He feels the urge to declare himself for an anthropomorphic approach to the problem. He writes: "I in my future work intend to go ahead imagining how, *if I were a rat, I* would behave as a result of such and such a demand combined with such and such an appetite and such and such a degree of differentiation, and so on." I mention this conclusion to demonstrate what kind of result must eventually be reached even by a man who has done such outstanding work in this field as Tolman has if he reviews critically the facts disclosed in innumerable experiments on animals.

Certainly any reaction is understandable only if we consider the individual phenomenon in reference to the condition of the whole organism. In animal psychology, too, such a conception has of late gained more ground. I should like to mention especially the work of K. S. Lashley and Kantor. A follower of Kantor, I. W. Carter, after a very careful analysis of all the different types of conceptions advanced for understanding the facts, holds that only an organismic or interactional conception, as he calls it, can do justice to the facts.[10] Thus he comes to the same conclusion as I did from my investigations in man: that the stimulus has to be considered from the point of view of "its stimulating function or value" for the individual, and that the response is an expression of the adjustment of the organism *as a whole* to the given situation. The special action by which this adjustment is reached is understandable, I would add, only in relation to the task which the organism faces at the moment, and in terms of the law that it is the organism's tendency to fulfill a task in such a way that its capacities are realized as fully as possible. This tendency represents the drive by which the organism is set going, a topic we shall have to discuss very soon.

We come to the conclusion therefore that what we usually call reflexes are performances of the organism which are understandable only from a knowledge of the organism. And thus we are brought back to the problem which the stimulus-response theory tried to solve.

Now what about conditioned reflexes?[11]

I need not say that we consider these phenomena as artificially produced and therefore cannot assume that normal life can be based on them. In saying this, however, I do not wish to deny that they may have significance in some special situations. We saw as we discussed proprioceptive reactions to abnormal tensions of single muscles that localized reactions may play an important role in situations of emergency and danger. Something similar may be the case with conditioned reflexes. We are very much interested in this problem, because the possible demonstration of such significance on the part of conditioned reflexes may teach us something about the role which artificial events play in normal life.

A look at the whole arrangement under which conditioned responses are built up and maintained shows clearly that the situation corresponds to what we have described as the characteristic requirement of isolated stimulus-response reactions in general. Conditioned responses are observed only when the organism as a whole is held in a definite constant state. In experiments this complicated situation is created and maintained by the experimenter.

I doubt whether in the natural life of an animal there can be such complicated conditions in the environmental situation as to build up conditioned reflexes, and, further, I doubt whether, if these conditions exist, they are constant enough to enable the conditioned responses to be maintained and thus become important for the life of the animal. Here is a problem which we have not enough experience to discuss. We can say somewhat more about the significance of conditioned responses in human children. Here, too, the experimenter, the educator, has to bring the infant into a situation which is suited for building up conditioned reflexes, and he has to maintain this condition for as long as the response is to be maintained. In immature children this is achieved by reward and punishment, but later the acquired actions can be preserved without these measures and by other factors, which are given in the *characteristic organization* of the human being. Two factors have to be considered. The first is the possibility of transition from a conditioned response to a natural, normal, adequate performance. For example, the baby must learn to control urination. He is not able to understand why, or how to manage it. Now a conditioned response may be built up by using reward and punishment, but later the habit is no longer based on these factors. His behavior comes to be determined by will, insight, and the purposeful use of his organic capacities — i.e., a special habit becomes part of the behavior as a whole that is characteristic of the grown child. Here the conditioned response shows its significance as a reaction built up in a state of immaturity as preparation for real performances in mature life. If this mature status is not achieved — because, for example, of retardation in the child's general, especially his mental, development — then the proper habit will never be perfectly attained. Conditioned responses are characteristic drill actions. Normal learned performances are not the result of *drill* but of *training*.

Both these proceedings aim at performances that are as good as possible. *Training* attempts to achieve them by exercising the natural capacities of the individual organism and by bringing them to the level of greatest efficiency. The performances in question are related to the nature of the organism, and the intended effect is the highest possible adequate relationship between the individual organism and the environment. In *drill* the performance aimed at is not related to the nature of the organism. It is achieved by building up a connection between a particular stimulus and a reaction by an *isolated* part of the organism. This connection, created by the method of conditioning, is intended to become so well set that whenever the stimulus is present the reaction appears automatically. The building up of such drill-reactions is possible only if the rest of the organism is in a definite situation which is held constant by certain means. In animals this is controlled by the trainer. Later the animal may be in a condition in which the isolation of parts required for conditioned responses occurs passively, without pain, but supported by reward and punishment. The best results are achieved, however, if the trainer uses performances which are natural to the animal. Then the performance will be executed most accurately and may also give the animal some pleasure. The best drills one sees in circuses are of this kind. An expert in drilling animals must be an expert in knowledge of their nature. In any case, the maintenance of the action demands the presence of the human being; it can never occur through the efforts of the animal itself.

In human beings as well, the best learning is
that which is based on the natural capacities of the
individual. Nevertheless, the human adult is also
forced to subject himself in some measure to learning
by drill. Because of the complex structure of
civilization, his environment is not consistently
natural. As a result, men are compelled to build
up external connections between certain stimuli and
definite reactions which make it possible for them to
respond to the sometimes very unnatural demands
of civilization.

There is a special capacity of human nature which
enables human beings to build up such unnatural
connections and to maintain them; it is the capacity
for abstraction. A human being is able to separate
functionally parts of his own organism from the
rest, subject them to specific isolated stimuli, and
let the reactions run off by themselves. In this way
he can drill himself. The only thing he has to do
is to avoid hindering these reactions. It is insight
into the necessity for such reactions which leads
the human being to build them up and to maintain
them. From this point of view it is obvious why
conditioned responses can be built up more easily
and maintained better in human beings than in
animals.

Thus we come to the conclusion that conditioned
responses cannot be considered as basic for understanding human behavior. They represent only
secondary phenomena; abstract behavior is necessary

for building them up and maintaining them. In animals they depend upon the experimenter's or trainer's capacity for abstraction; in infants on that of the educator; and in adult men on their own. This interpretation of conditioned reflexes in no way conflicts with our conclusions about unconditioned reflexes. True, conditioning is an essential factor in human behavior which must not be neglected. It can be used successfully, however, only if we consider it within the framework of the organism as a whole.

Our discussion of the stimulus-response theory has revealed that it is impossible to understand the behavior of organisms in terms of constant reactions of isolated apparatuses to external stimuli. We have always been brought back to the organization of the individual organism as a whole. We come to the same result if we try to understand human behavior on the basis of the so-called *instincts*.

I am sorry that I have no time here to analyze in detail the phenomena which are called instinctive behavior.[12] A careful analysis leads to the conclusion that these phenomena are of various kinds. Some — the reactions of infancy, as, for example, the to-turning reactions or the first grasping and sucking movements — are reactions caused through the immaturity of the organism; they represent the equalization processes of immature living matter. For their understanding the assumption of special instincts is not necessary. A second group — sitting, walking, speaking, etc.— represents performances of the same order as any other performance. They also are grounded in inborn potentialities and developed through experience. They have to be distinguished from other performances only by the fact that inborn and non-conscious factors play a much greater role than in other performances — than, for example, in the highest form of performance, voluntary actions. Although the latter, too, are based upon inborn potentialities, they are determined to a much higher degree by experience and learning. In a voluntary action the "drive" works through the medium of intention, thinking, decision, and motivation on the part of the individual; in an instinctive action the performance is set going directly by the "drive." Both types of performance are dependent, however, upon the activity of the organism as a whole. The third and last group of instinctive actions is made up of habits and customs, actions which are distinguished from other performances by the fact that they occur in relative isolation from the organism and thus seem to represent a special type. They are actions acquired by the activity of the whole organ which later gain a great independence of it.

In common with the voluntary actions, all these so-called "instinctive" actions represent the organism's means for coming to terms with the outer world in an adequate way; they make possible the organism's actualization of its capacities. They differ from voluntary actions, however, in the variety of capacities which are actualized under various conditions.

The tendency to actualize itself is the motive which sets the organism going; it is the *drive* by which the organism is moved. This idea about drives is in contradiction to most theories of drives, which assume (1) that the goal of the drive is to release itself, to release the tension which corresponds to it, and (2) that a number of different drives exists. In my opinion both assumptions are wrong. What can we learn from the observation of patients with brain injuries in connection with a theory of drives?

First, that the tendency to release tension is a characteristic phenomenon of pathological life. In pathology abnormal tensions occur relatively often in single fields, because reactions tend to take place in isolated parts and because the process of equalization is disturbed. Through abnormal tensions with which the organism cannot cope, catastrophic situations are favored. The sick person has the tendency to avoid catastrophic reactions, and therefore has a special tendency to remove abnormal tensions. This gives the impression that he is governed by a drive to do this. For example, the sick who suffer from a tension in the sex sphere seem to be forced to release this tension. From this observation the idea has arisen that it is the real goal of all drives to lift and discharge tension, and to bring the organism into a state of non-tension — i.e., that it is the goal of the drive to release itself.

The tendency to discharge any tension whatsoever is a characteristic expression of a defective organism, of disease. It is the only means the sick organism has to actualize itself, even if in an imperfect way. But the entire existence of a sick organism depends upon other organisms. Clearly, life under such conditions is not normal, and the mere discharge of tensions cannot therefore be characteristic of normal life. Innumerable instances teach us that it is the basic tendency of the sick organism to utilize what capacities it has in the best possible way (considered, of course, in relation to the normal nature of the organism concerned). The behavior of patients with brain injuries, for example, is to be understood only from such a point of view. A comparison of the behavior of our patients with that of normal persons leaves us no doubt that the life of the normal organism is also governed by this rule. We may say, then, that an organism is governed by the tendency to actualize its individual capacities as fully as possible. This tendency is frequently regarded as a tendency to maintain the existent state, to preserve oneself. We learn from pathology, however, that the tendency to self-preservation is characteristic of sick people and is a sign of anomalous life, of decay of life. For the sick person the only form of actualization of his capacities which remains is the maintenance of the existent state. This is not the tendency of the normal person. Sometimes, it is true, the normal organism also tends primarily to avoid catastrophes and to maintain a state which makes this possible, but this occurs only when conditions are unfavorable and is not at all the usual behavior. Under adequate conditions the tendency of normal life is toward activity and progress.

Since the tendency to actualize itself as fully as possible is the basic drive, the only drive by which the sick organism is moved, and since the life of the normal organism is determined in the same way, it is clear that the goal of the drive is not a discharge of tension, and that we have to assume only one drive, the drive of self-actualization. Under various conditions various actions come into the foreground; and since they seem thereby to be directed toward different goals, they give the impression of existing independently of each other. In reality, however, these various actions occur in accordance with the various capacities which belong to the nature of the organism, and in accordance with those instrumental processes which are the necessary prerequisites of the self-actualization of the organism.

The concept of different separate drives [13] is based on observations of the sick, of young children, and of animals under experimental conditions — that is, on observations made under circumstances in which some activities of the organism are isolated from the whole. This is the case in pathology; it is the case in children because the organism of the child lacks a center; and it is the case in experiments with animals because of the experimental conditions. One of the basic errors of the Freudian theory is that the tendencies observable in sick people are considered as the basic drives of the normal human being.

The impression that there are separate drives arises easily because the organism is governed at one time by one tendency, at another time by another, because one or the other tendency in a given condition becomes more important for self-actualization. This is especially the case when the organism is living under inadequate conditions. If a human being is forced to live in a state of hunger for a long time, or if there are conditions in his body which produce a strong feeling of hunger, so that he is urged to relieve this feeling, it disturbs the actualization of his whole personality. Then it appears as if he were under a hunger drive. The same may be the case with sex. A normal organism, however, is able to repress the hunger feeling or the sex urge if it has something very important to do, the neglect of which would bring the whole organism into danger.

The behavior of a normal individual is to be understood only if considered from the point of view that those performances are always fulfilled which are most important for the organism. This presupposes a normal centering of the organism and a normal, adequate environment. Because these conditions are not always fulfilled, even in normal life, the organism may often appear to be governed transitorily by a special tendency. In this case we have to deal with an emergency situation, not with a normal one, and as a result one gets the impression of a special, isolated drive. This is to be found particularly if the organism is not allowed to actualize one potentiality or another for an abnormally long time, as, for example, if the reception of food is hindered for a long time. Then the harmonious relationship between the organism and the outer world is thrown out of gear, and the individual is driven to fulfill that particular potentiality because only in this way can its existence be guaranteed. We are confronted here with a behavior corresponding to that in which only the activities prevail that are important for mere existence in situations of danger. But these are not the activities by which normal behavior can be understood.

On the basis of our discussion I believe we are in no way forced to assume the existence of special drives. I believe that the facts which are taken as foundations for the assumption of different drives are more or less abstractions from the natural behavior of the organism. They are special reactions in special situations, and represent the various forms by which the organism as a whole expresses itself.

The traditional view assumes various drives which

come into the foreground under certain conditions. We assume only one drive, the drive of self-actualization, but are compelled to concede that under certain conditions the tendency to actualize one potentiality is so strong that the organism is governed by it. Superficially, therefore, our theory may not appear to be much in conflict with the others, but I think there is an essential difference. From our standpoint we can understand the latter phenomenon as an abnormal deviation from normal behavior under definite conditions, but the theory of separate drives can never comprehend normal behavior without positing another agency which makes the decision in the struggle between the single drives. This means that any theory of drives has to introduce another, a "higher" agency. Here the same situation confronts us as in the discussion of reflexes, and we must again reject the auxiliary hypothesis as unsuitable in solving the problem. In the tendency of the organism to actualize itself we are faced with only one question. We do not need drives.

We reject the theory of drives from yet another point of view. If one of these potentialities,* or one which we can abstract from the whole of the organism, is taken as a distinct faculty, we fall into the errors of faculty psychology. It is isolated, and isolation changes the capacity, exaggerates it, just

* Henceforth the terms "potentiality" and "capacity" will be used interchangeably.

as it changes every behavioral aspect taken apart from the rest of the organism. If we start from the phenomena to be observed in such situations of isolation, we can never understand behavior. False concepts arise, as of the determining importance of single drives, sex or power, etc. A judgment about such phenomena as sex and power is to be made only if one considers them outside of their appearance in isolation and looks at their appearance in the natural life of the organism, where they present themselves as embedded in the activities of the *organism as a whole*. With this approach to the problem, the way — usually obstructed by some preconceived idea of isolated drives — is free for new investigations. This should be the essential outcome of our critique.

What are usually called drives are tendencies corresponding to the capacities and the nature of the organism, and to the environment in which the organism is living at a given time. It is better to speak of "needs." The organism has definite potentialities, and because it has them it has the need to actualize or realize them. The fulfillment of these needs represents the self-actualization of the organism. Driven by such needs, we experience ourselves as active personalities and are not passively impelled by drives that are felt to conflict with the personality.

A special form of such self-actualization is the need to complete incomplete actions, a tendency which explains many of the activities of the child. In the innumerable repetitions of children we are not dealing with the manifestation of a senseless drive for repetition but with the tendency toward completion and perfection. The driving force is given in the experience of imperfection, be it thirst, hunger, or the inability to fulfill any performance which seems to be within our capacities; the goal is the fulfillment of the task. The nearer we are to perfection, the stronger is the need to perform. This is valid for children as well as for adults.

The urge to perfection brings about the building up of more or less perfect instruments in any field. These in themselves become a further impulse for the use of the instrumental mechanisms, because this makes possible perfection in other fields. As long as the child's walking is imperfect, he tends to walk and walk, often with no other goal than walking. After he has perfected the walking, he uses it in order to reach a special point which attracts his attention — that is, to complete another performance, and so on.

It has been believed that it is possible to reduce drives to these instrumental mechanisms. The mechanisms themselves are supposed to have originated from conditioned responses built up by the organism as a means of adjustment during development. A drive, then, is nothing but a neural process or a habit corresponding to the neural process that releases these mechanisms. There is no doubt that habits lead to activity. But the problem is how these habits originate, and whether, for their acquisition, a special activity and tendency is not the necessary cause. There are two possibilities to be considered. Either the mechanisms develop with the maturation of inborn neural patterns without any active interference on the part of the organism, or they are built up by the activity of the organism in connection with experience. Nobody doubts that the development of mechanisms is based upon inborn dispositions corresponding to the nature of the organism, upon inborn capacities which develop with maturation. But the question is whether these capacities develop without any activity on the part of the organism. I think experience teaches us that this is not the case. The development of the mechanisms takes place as part of the organism's procedure in coming to terms with the outer world. Walking and speaking do not develop without an impulse on the part of the child. If this impulse is lacking, the development even of these definitely inborn capacities is retarded or missing. Thus the development of the mechanisms presupposes the drive for self-actualization, notwithstanding the "functional autonomy" the mechanisms achieve later on.

From these mechanisms arises a strong impulse toward action. They become instrumental in the performances of the organism and make the self-actualization of the organism easier; therefore there

is a strong urge to use them. Thus far we agree with
R. S. Woodworth,[14] who has emphasized the fact
that "the means to the end becomes an object of
interest on its own account." But normally this
"functional autonomy," as Allport has called it,[15] is
meaningfully integrated with the whole of the
personality; that is, "means to an end," "mechanisms," and "habits" achieve independence only
in so far as they are not in conflict with the "needs"
of the whole organism and the life situation. Whenever they gain an actual autonomy, then we are
dealing with a quite different phenomenon, with
unnatural isolation. This applies also to the habits
of groups — i.e., to customs. In the course of history
many customs, habits, and symbols in civilization
and culture have attained a certain emancipation
from their original contextual intention and govern
the behavior of the individual without his being
aware of their original purpose. Notwithstanding
the unjustified tyranny they may exercise and the
obstacles they may offer to free development, they
are still embedded within the purposive setting
of the situations and social framework in which
they play a part. If, however, this emancipation
reaches such a degree in individuals that the
mechanisms become practically detached from the
personality, then we have to do with pathological
conditions, with a consequent defective centering of
the organism.

ON THE MOTIVES ACTUATING
HUMAN BEHAVIOR

THE DISCUSSION of reflexes, instincts, and drives has established our contention that human behavior is intelligible only as viewed in connection with the organism as a whole. The particular emphasis which we have placed upon the abstract attitude as a conscious phenomenon may give the impression that we fail to pay tribute to non-conscious events. Now it is beyond doubt that human behavior cannot be understood on the basis of consciousness alone but that it embraces a great number of events of which we are not conscious. Usually one speaks of the "unconscious" factors by which human behavior is determined; I prefer to use the term "non-conscious." I am especially induced to discuss these non-conscious phenomena because in no field of psychology does so much confusion prevail as here, even with regard to the elementary facts.

The non-conscious events which, with the conscious ones, determine our acting and thinking are of various kinds. First, there are bodily processes, automatisms (as, for instance, expressive bodily patterns, postures), which support and facilitate appropriate mental and bodily sets initiated by voluntary activity, and thereby guarantee the execution of performances. These processes as such can never become conscious; they can be recognized only indirectly by the way of perception, just as we perceive objects in the outer world.

The second group of non-conscious events consists of inner experiences, commonly described as feelings, moods, attitudes, desires, needs, etc. We may, for example, have the experience of liking or disliking something, of finding something agreeable or disagreeable, of feeling harmony or disharmony, of being under tension or relaxed. This inner state is experienced, but can never become conscious in the correct sense of the term.

A proper appreciation of the facts demands a short comment here on the use of the term "consciousness." Very often it has been understood to mean the sum of all the contents of the mind of which we are aware, and these are regarded as being in a special realm, as if contained in a receptacle. We speak of consciousness only when we wish to denote behavior in which we are aware of what we are experiencing, or, as we might say, when we are "having" something consciously. We have a clear-cut awareness of a given situation, of our activity, of its purpose and its effect. The world then is experienced as apart from us, and we experience ourselves as objects equivalent to other objects. The states mentioned in the paragraph above, indeed, are experienced by the subject, too, but they are not objectified — that is, they are not conscious in the sense described above. If we try to become aware of them in this way, we have to transform them into objects, and then their original character of attitudes, feelings, etc., is lost, and they are distorted into "things." The mere fact that we can reflect upon a subjective state as if we were considering an object has led to the belief that these inner states can become "conscious," but actually this is impossible.

The third group of non-conscious events consists of the after-effects of earlier conscious events, which have been forgotten but which influence our present thinking and acting, with or without our being aware of their influence. These phenomena correspond to what we call memory.

Now, in a person whose behavior is conscious, there are always — in addition to those phenomena which we have called conscious — attitudes, bodily processes, and after-effects of earlier conscious phenomena. Or, to speak more correctly, all these phenomena — conscious and non-conscious — together, in a definite configuration, characterize conscious behavior. The singling out of any one of these behavioral aspects is a mere abstraction, because each of them represents an artificially isolated aspect of the *total* behavior. Sometimes it may seem as if they were separate entities — namely, whenever one of these aspects of total behavior is in the foreground, as figure, and the others form the background. Which aspect of the unitary behavior becomes the figure depends upon the situation, upon the kind of adjustment demanded from the organism as a whole. That aspect comes into the foreground which makes possible the optimal coming to terms of the organism with a given condition.

The normal course of thinking can take place only in a certain attitude, in a certain setting, and in a certain bodily state. Disturbances in the normal state of the attitudes or bodily processes derange the conscious actions, thought, will power, and so on. In the same way, attitudes and even bodily processes may be deranged by any disturbance in the voluntary conscious actions. Finally, disturbances of attitudes bear consequences for the bodily processes, and vice versa. A normal action of the organism demands a normal configuration of the activity of the organism as a whole, a configuration in which we can discriminate only abstractly the three aspects mentioned.

Each activity of the organism leaves an after-effect which modifies subsequent reactions, their course and intensity; the after-effect is strengthened when the organism is touched again by the same stimulus situation. Remembering and recalling, however, are bound to more specific conditions. Not all that we have once experienced affects later reactions or can be remembered in the same way. Remembrance to some extent presupposes a similarity between the situation of the organism at the time of the experience and a later condition. To put it more precisely: an event can be remembered only in that modality in which it first appeared. Now remembrance is normally bound to the figure; the background normally comes out in the after-effect only in conjunction with the figure to which it belongs. Thus the aspect which was originally the figure can affect behavior in a similar situation later. If this aspect is conscious in the sense given above, it can become effective later only in the form of a conscious phenomenon, influencing other conscious phenomena. If it is an inner experience, it can be effective later only in the form of an attitude or a feeling — that is, as an emotional setting, influencing other settings. Thus a phenomenon which is not experienced in a conscious form can never subsequently become directy conscious; and, conversely, a conscious phenomenon can never work directly upon attitudes or feelings. There is no direct transition from one aspect to the other, nor does a direct effect of one upon the other exist. Only by way of the whole, by a detour, so to speak, can either influence, arouse, or disturb the other.

In ordered life, after-effects occur in a way adequate to the tasks set before the individual. Normal behavior is built up from the reactions of the individual at a given moment and from those after-effects which favor his coming to terms with the outer world in the best possible way. Thus, the normal development of knowledge, of feelings, attitudes, habits, bodily processes, automatisms, skillful actions, and so on, is the result both of the reactions of the moment and of past experience.

There is an abnormal form of after-effect, however, which may disturb or even distort the behavior of the whole. Such distortion may be caused in each of the three aspects of behavior. For example, changes in the normal functioning of certain nervous apparatuses because of disease may produce as secondary changes abnormal effects in the bodily sphere, and this changed bodily background may distort feeling and thinking, as the subcortical changes in postencephalitis do. Abnormally exaggerated ideas or images derange conscious life and with it, secondarily, mental attitudes and bodily processes. Since conscious phenomena form the background for feelings and bodily processes, any derangement of conscious activity must also modify these phenomena. This is the case in some mental diseases. Finally, we know of after-effects which are the result of abnormal feelings, attitudes, etc. On these we must dwell in more detail because here we are dealing with influences to which the term "unconscious" has been especially applied.

These after-effects stem from situations in which the organism is not able to react in an adequate way. Phenomena then become isolated and attain an abnormal strength. These isolated phenomena have abnormal after-effects. If, in spite of these disturbing influences, the organism regains order, they may remain essentially in the background. However, in a condition where for other reasons the organism comes into a state of disequilibrium — that is, undergoes defective centering — these phenomena enter the foreground abnormally.

Abnormal after-effects always grow out of isolation. They originate in childhood as sequelae of the immaturity of the organism, and in adult life from conditions in which the demands made upon the organism exceed its capacities.

The infant responds to any stimulation that is at all effective with a reaction of the whole organism;[1] for example, his whole body turns in response to a light-stimulus. As he grows older, there are more and more reactions of individual apparatuses; that is, more and more figures stand out to which a corresponding functioning of the rest of the organism belongs as background. Now he reacts to the light-stimulus by a turning movement of the eyes alone, the rest of his body not participating overtly in this movement. Furthermore, in the earlier stage of development the child's reactions differ from those of adults in the fact that they consist predominantly of processes in the bodily sphere and of inner experiences, and not, for the most part, of conscious phenomena. The "figures" at that time correspond rather to what we call feelings, attitudes, needs, etc., than to conscious experience. On the other hand, all the phenomena found in the child are very intensive, have abnormal duration and stronger bonds to external stimuli, and represent both more primitive reactions and reactions in alternating phases; that is, they show the characteristics of phenomena in isolation. The prevalence of isolated phenomena is caused by the fact that the reactions occur in an immature organism, where the relationship of individual reactions to each other and to the organism as a whole is not fully developed. The normal configuration of an organismic event presupposes the organism's maturity. The criterion of maturity is a proper centering; this requires the abstract attitude, by virtue of which all mental and behavioral aspects can be properly integrated and thus adequately centered in the personality as a whole.

The life of the infant is always precarious. Because of his immature state, most of the stimuli originating in the world surrounding him do not yet "fit" his organism; they demand reactions that belong to a more mature, more fully integrated organism. In consequence, the organism of the child is very often unable to accomplish the required actions in an adequate, ordered way. His tendencies, feelings, attitudes, come into conflict with what is demanded of him; there is a clash between his tendency to self-realization, which corresponds to his immature state, and what is forbidden. If, however, the adults representing the child's environment take such immaturity into consideration and try to avoid situations not commensurate with his degree of maturity, then he may gradually adapt himself to their demands and prohibitions by behavioral adjustments and attitudes which arise from development and training, especially with the help of his increasing capacity for abstraction. What we said in our discussion of conditioned reflexes about the development of habits may be recalled here. The child may acquire adequate habits — especially when consciousness enables it, if necessary, to bear voluntarily even something disagreeable — because they seem appropriate and useful for the actualization of its personality.

Thus the normal development of the child proceeds by way of adaptation through its maturing and training. Such attitudes and urges as are in opposition to the development of the whole personality disappear and become ineffective because of the development of adequate habits. Consequently we find not continuous repression but continuous formation of new patterns. As the child matures, new patterns of the organism are formed, conforming to the ways of the human species in general and to the cultural pattern of the particular milieu in which the child grows up. Of course one may call this development "ego formation," and of course the prohibitions the child meets with, like other processes in the environment, are co-determining factors. Yet the effects of former reactions are not *forgotten* through repression; rather, they *cannot be remembered*, because they are no longer part of the attitudes of later life, and therefore cannot become effective. Though it may be that some reactions are repressed voluntarily, voluntary repression is certainly not important in childhood: first, because conscious behavior is developed only to a small degree; further, because voluntary repression requires a very strong will, and even then is usually not very successful. There is undoubtedly less voluntary repression in childhood than there is of building up of new and adequate habits. Their development makes for a passive disappearance of the older inadequate reactions and leads to their fading away into the background.

If the child is forced to do things that are too difficult for him, however, then catastrophic situations and anxiety set in, and he attempts to avoid these situations through substitute reactions. He tends to resort to those attitudes of which he is capable (that is, the more primitive ones), because he feels himself protected by these against the endangering demands; or he builds up new habits which allow escape from anxiety. He is not conscious of these tendencies and usually develops them in the way we have described in patients who lack the capacity for abstraction. Because of their isolation from the total personality these attitudes have a disturbing influence and may hinder the further development of the child. Since they do not belong to the subsequent developmental stages they upset behavior and are experienced as strange to the individual. Like all isolated phenomena, they are especially likely to produce an ambivalent state. If not overcome by later centering, this ambivalent mental set produced by a particular situation in childhood may influence the activity of the adult.

As long as the individual achieves a certain adaptation to life in spite of abnormal habits and ambivalence — that is, comes to terms with the world to some degree — these peculiarities may be considered as disagreeable things which have to be borne. If later, however, in adult life, situations arise with which the individual is not able to cope and which produce phenomena of isolation, weakness of centering, and ambivalence, then the old disturbing after-effects may come to the foreground in an abnormal way. If these are not conscious phenomena, the distortion is regarded as produced by the invasion of the unconscious. When these after-effects have an abnormal influence, ambivalence increases more and more. The patient may be in permanent danger of running into catastrophic situations; anxiety leads him to search for new outlets; and gradually a neurotic condition develops.

For various reasons the patient is not conscious of the origin of the symptoms arising from this condition: (1) the phenomena which disturb him have the character of attitudes, feelings, needs, etc., which, as such, have never been "conscious"; (2) he tries to repress the attitudes which produce anxiety because they do not fit his present life-situation and personality make-up. This may happen in the adult without conscious awareness; in the same way, he may repress a conflict of the present because he is not able to solve it.

Now, if we offer him protection against his rising anxiety, as during therapy, he reveals his ambiva-

lence in various ways — by expressive movements,
affective excitation, outbursts, moods of depression,
and so on. And, of course, he may also express his
feelings in words. When free associations are elicited,
especially, he may utter all that corresponds to his
present and former state of ambivalence, to wishes,
feelings, attitudes, thoughts, and ideas that belong
both to childhood and to the present. It is often not
easy to distinguish which of the phenomena belong
to the present, which to the earlier, conflict — which
represent the real conflict of the patient, and which
are only means that later increase it and lead to its
outbreak. Usually all the ideas expressed are considered as emerging from infancy, as having been
repressed at that time into the so-called "unconscious." It is assumed to be the task of the psycho-
therapist to make conscious the repressed ideas which
produced conflict in infancy, because to this conflict
is attributed the chief reason for the development of
the present conflict and thus for the appearance of
the symptoms.

Here arises the fatal mistake of psychoanalysis.[2]
Many of the ideas expressed during free association
may allude to the feelings, attitudes, and needs of
infancy, but they are couched in the language of
adult experience. There is no reason to conclude
from the observable facts that these ideas have lived
in the patient's unconscious since his early childhood.
The fact that they frequently have contents which
could never have belonged to a child utterly refutes

such a conclusion. That some few of the ideas may
have had their origin in the thinking of childhood,
and that this can be disclosed as the cause of abnormal reactions and of later symptoms, does not conflict
with our statement. The cases in which this occurs
are of a special type. For instance, the adult has
forgotten the once-conscious conflict; yet some habits
connected with its overcoming persist, and they disturb him later in situations where they occupy the
foreground without his realizing their presence. If in
such cases the forgotten situations are made conscious — and this can be done, because they were
conscious in infancy — then it is relatively easy to
free the patient from his abnormal habits and from
the concomitant disturbance of his life.

This is not so easy in those cases in which the
basis of the disturbance does not consist of forgotten
conscious phenomena but of feelings, attitudes, needs,
which did not fit the life-situation in the early stages
of development. Such a conflict usually results in
the development of the severe neurosis. Here the
inadequacy of the feelings is the disturbing factor,
and improvement is difficult because feelings which
have never been conscious cannot be made conscious.
What psychotherapy can do here is to bring the individual into a situation in which these feelings emerge
without the patient's having to be afraid of them as
he was in childhood, because now he experiences
them under the protection of the therapeutic situation. This protection enables him to face his feelings

and to see that they belong to the state of infancy
and have nothing directly to do with his present condition. He realizes that the disturbances are caused
by factors which were isolated from his personality
in the past and which have brought about phenomena
that are apart from his present personality. He
overcomes their influence by realizing that they do
not belong to the present conflict and that they hinder
him from solving it — and this is the prime effect of
the analysis. If we succeed in making him aware of
this situation, he is forced to occupy himself with the
present conflict and is able to solve it by finding a
new adaptation.

Getting rid of these influences becomes more difficult the more one considers them as effects of definite
forces which live in a special realm of the unconscious
and which emerge to disturb the individual, without
his being able to enter this realm and fight the forces
there. Such a hypostatization of the after-effects of
needs and feelings, and particularly the application
of definite names to them, makes a liberation from
them highly difficult, if not impossible. Psychoanalytic interpretation, which is full of such hypostati-
zations, often leads to this result. On the other hand,
it does not make a definite distinction between the
phenomena belonging to the present state of the individual and those belonging to childhood; consequently it creates a wrong attitude on the part of the
individual toward the effects of his earlier life. In
overemphasizing the events of childhood it fails to

see that motivation and conflict are always contemporary, or, as Gordon Allport says, that motivation always has to be tackled from the condition as present. This faulty overemphasis upon the genetic approach to the study of conflicts has even begun to arrest the attention of psychoanalysts themselves. For example, Karen Horney writes: "I believe that the genetic approach if used onesidedly [and I add, as is the case in Freudianism] confuses rather than clarifies the issue, because it leads then to a neglect of the actually existing unconscious tendencies and their functions and interactions with other tendencies that are present, such as impulses, fears, protective means." [3] The astonishing thing is that the author fails to realize that with this statement she drifts away from the essentials of the theory of psychoanalysis and deprives it of its real basis.

This overestimation of the genetic factor, on the one hand, and the misinterpretation of the ideas presented in free association as being repressed conscious phenomena, on the other, have had a fateful consequence in both a theoretical and a practical respect. They have induced the analyst to look again and again for explanations of the ideas expressed (usually selected in a very uncritical way from the free associations of the patient), and as a result many theoretical statements of psychoanalysis have arisen which lead only to the hopeless struggle of the neurotic patient with psychoanalytic terms, a situation that suggests the vain labor of Sisyphus.

With this critical probing of the concept of the unconscious, many other essential points of the theory of psychoanalysis become doubtful. Since it is not my purpose to scrutinize psychoanalysis here, however, I must confine myself to these comments. Our problem was the unconscious, and thus we had to take issue with the Unconscious in the psycho-analytic sense.

In the light of our discussion non-conscious phenomena take on a character that is totally different from the one psychoanalysis ascribes to them. We divorce them from their negative denotation as re-pressed conscious phenomena, charged with the tendency to reoccupy the forbidden grounds of con-sciousness; indeed, we try to acknowledge them as events of a positive, unartificial, and observable na-ture. Finally we attempt to evaluate their signifi-cance for and influence upon behavior, be it normal or pathological. With this we avoid the wrong hypostatization of functional (i.e., configurational) events to separate driving forces, which is so charac-teristic of the Freudian theory; we thereby escape the wrong theory of drives, as well as the false over-estimation of single factors which determine life — for example, sex.

Let me add to our discussion of the unconscious some remarks about the epistemological basis of Freud's theory, from which alone his point of view becomes really understandable. The underlying pro-cedure is akin to the one we met in our discussion of the reflex theories. In these theories we encountered the erroneous premise that the partitive phenomena gained by atomistic methods represent facts from which we can gain a direct understanding of the behavior of the organism and that we can synthesize these elements again to form a concept of the organism as a whole. We find the same kind of procedure in psychoanalysis, especially in its evaluation of findings in the free association experiment, which is a typical example of the isolating procedure, since the subject is instructed to say the first thing that enters his mind, neglecting as much as possible its relation to his personality.

If one considers the materials produced through free association as facts, one is in the same position as if one considered all individual responses to stimuli as building-stones for the understanding of the behavior of an organism, and then one runs into the difficulties which arise if one neglects the rules governing the procedure of isolation. In psychoanalysis the same kind of attempt is made to overcome these difficulties as in the reflex theories — namely, by building up a series of auxiliary hypotheses. It was in this way that the theory of drives originated, and especially the overvaluation of a sex drive. Misjudging the relationship between individual phenomena and the organism as a whole, Freud conceived the idea of a hierarchy of antagonistic mental elements, such as the subconscious, the conscious, the ego, and the super ego, and converted certain phenomena which appear in the behavior of the organism into factors which govern that behavior. Especially unfortunate were his failure to take into consideration the fact that all the phenomena on which his theory was based had been observed in people who were not in a normal state, and his neglect of the fact that it is not permissible to transfer or apply directly to normal people an evaluation derived from such phenomena.

Here again, in spite of its striking difference from the other psychology of the late nineteenth century, the Freudian form of thinking reveals its origin in the same epistemological background and reflects the same methodological errors as any other pure positivistic-atomistic approach. I have stressed the methodological errors which, in my opinion, underlie the theory of psychoanalysis because only by having recourse to them can a critique be pertinent and fruitful.

Freud's theory of the unconscious has its effect on his appreciation of the conscious. As we saw before, his theory made him fail to recognize the significance of conscious phenomena. Before Freud, psychology suffered from an overrating of the conscious, and it advocated a conception of consciousness in terms of a realm with separate contents and with atomistic laws regarding their functions. This attitude was combined with a neglect of non-conscious phenomena, which were considered essentially negative. In Freud, on the other hand, we find an overrating of the unconscious, which is conceived of as a realm that has both content and rules of activity, while conscious phenomena are neglected and in their turn considered essentially negative. Neither tendency is in keeping with the facts. Just as a proper recognition of the non-conscious is necessary, so an appreciation of consciousness is necessary if we wish to understand human behavior. A comparison between normal persons and those with brain diseases leads one to realize the positive importance of consciousness and to appreciate the special endowment which consciousness imparts to man and which distinguishes him from all other living nature. No matter how many performances patients with brain diseases are still capable of accomplishing, they lack every creative power, the most characteristic in human nature. It is precisely this factual material of pathology that impresses us with the enormous significance of consciousness.

On the other hand, of course, our standpoint has certain implications for therapeutic practice. A critical elaboration of psychoanalytic material and theory is bound to uncover sooner or later a nucleus of facts which will reveal itself as similar in principle to the basic types of organismic laws which a more truly biological approach discloses. I have mentioned many phenomena in our patients which might be described in psychoanalytic terms, but they are described more simply and with fewer prepossessions in biological terms. The similarity in principle between the behavior of what we call "organic" patients and neurotics will become more and more understandable from the point of view that in both cases we are dealing with expressions of biological events, which are governed by the same fundamental laws. If I preferred to make organic pathology my starting point, I did so because the material it offers is easier to study and the conclusions drawn from it are less exposed to fallacies than those of psychoanalysis. When we shall have reached the phase in which we interpret organic and psychogenic cases from a common biological standpoint, then many of Freud's ideas will be found to retain their importance, and his great merit in leading toward a truer understanding of the nature of man will receive its deserved appraisal. With all my criticism, I do not wish to give the impression that I am blind to the enormous merits of Freud. Yet even a genius is a child of his time. If I see it correctly, it was Freud's fate not to achieve the goal of understanding human behavior to its very depths — a goal to which he came nearer than anyone else — because of his preoccupation with certain prejudices of the natural science of his time.

Our approach endeavors to open the way for the discovery, without theoretical bias, of the essential conflicts which ultimately bring about disease. The conflict has to be understood on the basis of the individual life-history, which contains bodily processes, attitudes, and conscious events. All these events have to be considered in their configurational relation within the given individual according to the situation in which they originally took place, and they have to be evaluated according to their present significance for the individual's coming to terms with his environment. When this approach is adopted, psychotherapy will lose much of its exciting, interesting character, but I think it can be brought nearer to simple truth and, because the duration of treatment will be lessened can be made more beneficial to the patient.

VII

ON THE STRUCTURE OF PERSONALITY

OUR ANALYSIS has disclosed some characteristic trends in the structure of the organism. We have seen the specific significance of the abstract attitude for human behavior, the relation between abstract and concrete behavior, and the role both play in human life. We have familiarized ourselves with the character of conscious and non-conscious events and the way they influence each other. We have become acquainted with some of the general rules that determine the human being's coming to terms with the outer world. We have learned that man is a being who does not merely strive for self-preservation but is impelled to manifest spontaneity and creativeness, that man has the capacity of separating himself from the world and of experiencing the world as a separate entity in time and space. All these features we have inferred from the changes which patients with brain injuries show as a result of the loss of various capacities.

In attempting to understand human behavior, however, we cannot content ourselves with these results so long as we are unable to determine the qualitative structure of the individual human organism in which reactions in a given situation are ultimately rooted. It will be remembered that in all our discussions we had to refer back to the potentialities of the organism as basic for all its activities. We arrived at the conclusion that the drive which sets the organism going is nothing but the forces which arise from its tendency to actualize itself as fully as possible in terms of its potentialities. But what are the potentialities of a given individual?

In making definite general statements about human potentialities we must be mindful of the fact that any such general statements are abstractions from what has been observed in individuals, and that we have learned nothing about how to investigate these potentialities. Unquestionably, we have to go back to concrete findings as offered by the isolating methods. But how, among the innumerable observable phenomena, shall we discriminate between those which really correspond to the nature of the individual and those which are only more or less accidental reactions produced by the method that has been used? To decide this question we are in need of a criterion. We are faced here with a problem which lies at the center of modern psychology, the problem of how to characterize personality.

Although for a time the study of personality was neglected to a marked degree by psychology, scholars are now at work in many places trying to find a way to comprehend it. I cannot describe these various attempts here, but those who wish to become thoroughly acquainted with the complexity of this problem and the multiplicity of the attempts to attack it will find Gordon W. Allport's *Personality: A Psychological Interpretation* an excellent guide. (In addition to giving an admirable critical review of the research methods in this field, the book presents a conception of Allport's own which is well worth following up.)

We can assume that those factors belong essentially to an organism which guarantee its existence. There is no question that, in spite of its changing in time and under varying conditions, an organism remains to a certain degree the same. Notwithstanding all the fluctuations of the behavior of a human being in varying situations, and the unfolding and decline that occur in the course of his life, the individual organism maintains a relative constancy. If this were not the case, the individual would not experience himself as himself, nor would the observer be able to identify a given organism as such. It would not even be possible to talk about a definite organism.

This is not the place to elaborate on the highly specialized and subtle controversies that center around the question of specificity versus consistency of traits, nor to reiterate the difficulties which the advocates of specificity have encountered and the criticisms which have been presented recently in various publications. I prefer to take another route. I should like to contribute to the discussion by drawing evidence in favor of consistency from a kind of material which is not so well known but through which biology can supplement psychology.

Consistency appears in pathology in a special form, in the abnormally ordered behavior of the patient. It is true that we have to deal here with a pathologically exaggerated phenomenon, but, as we have explained above, the tendency to ordered behavior belongs to the normal organism as well. Consequently, in their content observable activities during ordered behavior can be considered as reflecting essential capacities belonging to the individual concerned.

If we consider an organism first in the usual atomistic way, as composed of parts, members, and organs, and then in its natural behavior, we find that in the latter case many kinds of behavior which on the grounds of the first consideration can be conceived of as possible are not actually realized. Instead, a definite selective range of kinds of behavior exists. These we shall classify as "preferred" behavior. To avoid possible misunderstanding it should be pointed out that this term does not imply any conscious awareness or choice of a special way of performing; it is merely descriptive of the observable type of behavior. The way in which the organism actually experiences this state of preferred behavior we shall describe later.[1]

To illustrate the phenomenon we have ample choice in the various fields of pathological human behavior, normal human behavior, and animal behavior. To mention one example in animal life, we know that a cat, when dropped, always lands on its feet. In spite of differing environmental situations it always returns to an optimally balanced position, and this we call the preferred position. If we turn the head of a cat toward one side we find an immediate compensation for this abnormal position, a turning back to the old position. Or, if this is prevented, the posture of the rest of the body changes until a definite total position is again achieved. Thus, within a certain range, the animal has the capacity of adapting itself to differing environmental situations through specific positions of the body. Certain definite positions and actions belong to the various activities of the animal — sitting, eating, sleeping, etc. The number of possible positions and performances becomes much larger in the higher animals, and especially in man. But even in human beings the possible positions and other modes of behavior by no means correspond in number to the organization of the members concerned, and to the quantitative variability of the environmental situation, as it appears in the usual analytical investigation.

The phenomena to which I wish to point first can be easily observed. Anyone can make the pertinent observations. If a person points to a place that lies more or less to the side, he does not always execute the pointing movement of the arm in the same manner. If the object at which he is pointing is slightly to the side, say to the right, he points only with his extended arm, without moving the rest of the body, in such a way that the angle between arm and the frontal plane of the body is obtuse, about 130° to 140°. If the object at which he is pointing lies more nearly in front of him, then the arm is no longer moved alone, but the trunk too is moved somewhat, toward the other side (the left), so that the pointing arm still forms approximately the same angle with the frontal plane of the body as before. If the object pointed at lies further to the side — say to the extreme right — then the body turns so far to the right that, when the subject points, the angle between the frontal plane and the arm is again essentially the same as before. Of course, it is possible to behave differently; for example, one can point forward while the body remains fixed. But this is not the natural way. In the pointing movement, then, the organism seems to have the tendency to prefer a definite relation between the positions of arm and trunk, and does not conform to the varying environmental demands, although this could very well be done by changing the relation between the arm and trunk positions. To take another example, if one asks a person who is standing to describe a circle, one type of individual usually describes a circle of medium size in a frontal plane parallel to the line of the body, using the index finger of the right hand, the arm being half flexed at the elbow. Larger circles and circles in other positions, possibly executed with the extended arm, seem unnatural and uncomfortable to such persons, who naïvely proceed in the manner we have described. When the trunk is bent forward, however, it is natural for this type to describe the circle in a horizontal plane. One might think the horizontal circle simply the result of the movement of the arm in the same relationship to the upper part of the body as before, and due only to the change in bodily position. If this were true, we should have a circle in an oblique plane; actually, however, it is in the horizontal plane. In this position, apparently, the circle in the horizontal plane corresponds to the preferred behavior. Accurate analysis shows that the manner of describing the circle is unequivocally determined by the *total* situation of the subject. In "total situation" the factor of the subject's attitude toward the task is included; consequently the circle is not made by all subjects in the same way. In a specific situation, however, each one makes it in a specific way which he prefers, quite naïvely, to all other possible ways.

Through this simple experiment one can detect some characteristic properties of individuals belonging to different types of personality. In the one type the objectifying attitude prevails. This type prefers to describe a small circle in an almost frontal parallel plane. Another type is more subjective and has a prevailing motor attitude. This type describes a large circle with the extended arm, with excessive movement in the shoulder joint; actually the subject does not describe a true circle, but moves his arm around in a circular fashion, for which an excessive excursion is most natural. These variations in the execution of the circle reveal differences between men and women, between persons of different character, vocations, and so on. But each person has his own preferred way of performing, and it is this that is essential for the point under discussion.

If one who is accustomed to hold his head somewhat obliquely is forced to hold it straight, it requires a special effort, and, in addition, after a certain time the head will return into the usual, "normal" position, unless the subject prevents this by continuously paying attention to the position of his head. If, in going to sleep, one assumes a variety of positions, one will very soon take a certain position which leads naturally to falling asleep. Much wakefulness is due simply to the fact that one is prevented by some circumstance from assuming this natural position. If we trace the causes for the assumption of such positions, we find a great variety of bodily and psychological factors, but they are almost always fixed for a given individual.

In abnormal persons such phenomena can be observed even better than in normal persons. We have stressed the fact that in our patients we are dealing with states of disintegration or decreased differentiation of personality. The reduced and narrowed personality of the patient is cut off from many events in the outer world which the normal person experiences; it is confined to a more limited order, as is shown by the tendency to abnormal orderliness as a means of avoiding catastrophes. In an organism thus reduced to a simpler form of organization and to a shrunken range of activities, preferred behavior comes strikingly to the foreground and it ought therefore to be easier to discover its qualitative characteristics.

There are two further circumstances which bring preferred behavior to the foreground in abnormal persons. A normal person, because of his capacity for abstraction and voluntary action, is able to execute tasks in a not-so-preferred condition and to maintain a not-preferred behavior. In addition, he is not restricted to the type of preferred behavior we have been discussing; he is capable also of preferred performances on a higher level, which correspond to his higher level of performance in general. The abnormal person is either wholly incapable of this, or less capable of it, because of his lack of the capacity for abstraction. As a consequence, he is subject in a higher degree to preferred behavior. This is manifest in the fact that a patient who is asked to execute a movement in an uncomfortable position invariably shifts into a more comfortable one unless his attention is concentrated entirely on the task demanded of him. To prevent such concentration it usually suffices to have him carry out the movement with closed eyes. We find then that, even against his will, and usually without his knowledge, he assumes the preferred position. The second circumstance is as follows. In normal persons preferred performances have a certain range of variability within which a performance is still adequate. In abnormal persons this realm is narrowed and the preferred perform-ances are restricted to more rigid positions and to more fixed relations between positions. Thus, for ex-ample, in a patient with a disturbance of the left frontal lobe, the preferred position of the head is a slight tilting to the right. This is his natural position. If the examiner brings the head into a straight posi-tion or tilts it to the left or even further to the right, the head returns without the subject's knowledge into the natural position, where it ultimately will remain. The same thing happens if the patient him-self intentionally holds his head in an abnormal posi-tion and then pays no further attention to it. A normal person can hold his head in a position that is to a certain degree oblique without discomfort and without having an irresistible tendency to bring the head back to its normal position. The patient is forced to bring his head back.

What we have said about these simple motor ac-tions is valid for all other performances. Every indi-vidual reveals preferences not only in the motor sphere, in walking, standing, sitting, eating, and so on, but in the sensory and intellectual processes, in the realm of feeling and voluntary activities. The perceptual field offers some interesting examples. When angles between 30° and 150° are presented optically, not all the steps of the differential threshold are experienced as equal. What we recognize primarily are acute, obtuse, and right angles. (The knowledge of these facts we owe especially to the investigations of Max Wertheimer [2] and other *Gestalt* psychologists.) These are the preferred impressions around which all others are grouped. Each of the preferred impressions has its range. An angle of 93°, for instance, appears as a poor right angle, deviating somehow from the preferred impression, and does not give the impression of uniqueness. In tachystoscopic experiments it is the circle which is easiest to recognize; polygonal figures are perceived as circles. The circle is also preferred tactually. In the common field of vision there is a preference for the square, for certain curves, symmetry against asymmetry, the vertical against a somewhat oblique line, and so on. Corresponding phenomena are found in the field of tones. The fourth and the fifth are preferred. Small deviations leave perception relatively unaffected. Larger deviations are experienced as an impurity of the fifth (as a bad fifth, etc.), without one's always being able to say in which direction the deviation occurs.

In pathology the assimilation of an oblique line to a vertical is particularly instructive. The line presented may deviate considerably from the objective vertical and still be experienced as a vertical. This becomes especially apparent when a patient sees the line as a vertical irrespective of whether it deviates to the right or to the left. When I showed one of my patients a stick one foot long at a distance of two yards, first in a vertical position and then in a ten-degree inclination to the left or to the right, he did not notice the difference, but saw only a vertical rod. (Correspondingly, a stick that deviated by ten degrees from the horizontal was always seen as horizontal. Only in deviations above ten degrees did the patient see that the stick was oblique.) When the stick was turned from the vertical into the oblique position he did not see the change until the stick reached the region where he could experience deviations.

The usual explanation of these phenomena even in normal persons as being the effects of past experience, habit, training, etc., has proved invalid. For material on the subject I may refer here to the numerous experiments in *Gestalt* psychology and to many published observations in pathology.

Performances under preferred conditions show two characteristics. (1) They represent the most exact execution of the required task under the circumstances given; for example, pointing in the preferred realm is much more exact than elsewhere. (2) They are executed with a feeling of comfort and ease, of fitness and adequacy. Natural performances under not-preferred conditions are experienced as disagreeable, unsatisfactory, unnatural.

As I have explained elsewhere,* observation shows that preferred performances are determined not only

* See p. 248, note 1 to Chapter VII.

by the processes in the area where we observe them but also by the condition of the rest of the organism. On the basis of many facts reported elsewhere I reached the conclusion that preferred behavior in one field always means preferred behavior on the part of the whole organism; the tendency toward preferred behavior is an expression of the fact that the organism constantly seeks a situation in which it can perform at its best and with optimal comfort. Preferred performances are the performances which correspond best to the capacities of the organism. Thus observation of such performances may serve as a means of finding out the capacities — the constants — of the organization and functioning of the individual. The problem of research on personality can thus be substantiated. We are only at the beginning of this kind of quest. Consequently, our discussion will have to deal more with possible methods of procedure in this new field than with a comprehensive survey of facts.

For our purposes we should have to explore an individual by exposing him to a variety of tasks in the fields of perception, motor performance, memory, thinking, and so on; in every instance we must seek to determine what are for him the preferred ways of execution. These consist not only of the actual patterns of the performance as determined from observed overt behavior but include the preferred mediums of execution, as, for instance, retention through the medium of visualization or through the medium of kinesthetic representation. For every task there is an objective optimal manner of adequate execution, and for every individual there is a certain range of possible variations within the realm of his preferences. Consequently, we may call the preferred way of execution a constant of the individual. Ultimately these constants are basic traits of the constitutional and character make-up of the individual. Wherever the individual does his best, notwithstanding the fact that another solution may be more adequate in the light of the objective optimal execution, we are dealing with a constant. Here we face a number of interesting psychological problems and educational implications upon which I can only touch in passing. Very likely the question of individual aptitudes — perhaps even the problem of intelligence — ought to be oriented by the measure to which objective adequacy and the subjective preferred way of performing approach each other.

In all these investigations, of course, we have to be mindful of certain positive and negative criteria.

1. No matter what the behavioral field in which we may test an individual, we are justified in speaking of a constant only when and if other pertinent tests show that, concomitantly with the execution in that field, the rest of the organism is in *ordered* condition; for example, definite behavior in a sensory field can be called constant only when we ascertain that, among other things, blood pressure, respiration, pulse

rate, threshold of reflexes, etc., correspond to the norm of the individual, which is to be determined for each field in the way just described.

2. If a required task falls outside the realm of the preferred ways that are peculiar to an individual, the corresponding capacity is wanting in a greater or less degree. In such a case we have to vary the methods of examination until the subject is able to cope with the task in some way that he finds natural. For example, an individual is subjected to a task for the execution of which visual memory is a prerequisite (e.g., he is asked to memorize a complicated path). Now we find that, if we try to impose the use of visual imagery, his general state becomes disturbed. But if we allow him to choose another means of coping with the task — for instance, memorizing by verbalization instead of visualization — then he may perform fairly well, and his general condition will remain undisturbed. He will verbalize, for example, in this way: "First I have to turn left, then go a hundred feet straight ahead, then turn to the right," and so on. The result is not, of course, so successful as it would be through visualization, which is better adapted to this particular task, but it is precisely because of this that the performance is so revealing to us. It indicates the patient's lack of capacity in the visual field and brings to light his preference for memorizing by language; another person may have another preference, drawing upon kinesthetic memory, for example. Thus this method may be instru-

mental in discovering the constants in individuals in certain types of performances.

3. The preferred and ordered behavioral forms (constants) are not identical in all the performances of an individual. On the contrary, the individual responds to every type of task in a special way. This is determined by the organism's tendency to come to terms with the requirements of the outer world in the best possible condition of the whole. This can be attained by various means in various tasks. Consequently, constants have to be determined through the discovery of the *types of task* which the individual can perform most successfully, as evidenced in his preferences. Of course, the circumstances under which a task is presented also have an influence in that they elicit differing preferred ways. But by varying and controlling these circumstances we can find out under what conditions an individual performs best and which of his preferred ways represents a true constant. For example, if a person is faced with a task under conditions which prescribe different speeds of execution, he may execute this task adequately within a certain range of speed but fail when other speeds are demanded. Now we can define his constant on the basis of the knowledge we have gained by introducing controlled circumstantial variables.

The constant in the temporal course of processes must be regarded as particularly characteristic of individuality. The important role of the specific temporal sequence of processes for the ordered activity of the normal organism can be seen in the fact that many pathological phenomena may be regarded as being predominantly the expression of changes in the normal temporal course. This is shown not only by the analysis of symptoms but also by investigations with time-measuring methods (e.g., chronaxie and electroencephalography). Every human being has his own rhythm. This rhythm manifests itself in various temporal measures in various performances, but in any given performance it is always in the same measure. A performance is normal only when an individual can accomplish it in the rhythm that is natural to him for this performance. This holds true for psychological events like emotion or thought processes or acts of will; it is also the case in physiological processes, like the beating of the heart and respiration, and in physicochemical processes. All these time constants indicate particular characteristics of the personality.

From my experience to date I believe that we are justified in selecting a number of factors as guiding for the determination of constants. We have pointed out that each person prefers a definite medium for the performance of certain tasks — for instance, a definite sense modality, or the motor apparatus, or speech; all this is indicative of certain constants. The preference for a concrete or an abstract approach falls under the same aspect.

But we must be careful not to relapse into the old

notion of visual, auditory, motor, and other types. The preference for a certain sensory medium in one field involves certain characteristics of behavior in fields other than the preferred one. These characteristics are not necessarily the same and may be of different natures although they are dependent upon preferences in other fields. They are ultimately embedded and rooted in a definite interactional organization of the personality as a whole. And we must inquire about the qualitative nature of this interaction. For example, if a person is preinclined to the concrete attitude, his behavior is very often accompanied by less emphasis on verbalization and language than is the case in the person preinclined to the abstract. In turn, the latter will fail to regard many details in his environment which do not elicit a language response. Again, the person with a tendency toward the abstract leans toward personalized emotional contacts with others; the person with a tendency toward the concrete is more given to objective realities in social contacts. I mention these examples in order to illustrate two points: (1) that preferred ways in one field influence and shape preferred ways in other fields; (2) that this influence does not occur by direct causation, nor does it manifest itself by uniform phenotypic symptoms, but rather indirectly, by way of the functional organization of the whole. The usual test approach fails here to consider the peculiar interactional dependence of all behavioral fields upon the personality structure as a whole. This complex relation remains to be explored and defined before we can draw conclusions from results in tests which are based on the erroneous premise that any capacity is a factor of *uniform* manifestation in *all* the activities of an individual. Obviously, all this has a bearing upon the much-discussed problem of types, as, for instance, the introvert-extrovert problem.

It is true that as yet we do not know very much about the determinants of the functional relation between a preferred performance in one field and performances in other fields. Pathology, however, has adduced empirical evidence to the effect that changes of constants in one field are accompanied by changes in other fields, so that we may reasonably infer from this material the functional interdependence we have suggested above.

Only on the basis of the knowledge of the structural interrelation between preferred performances in various fields can the problem of what are called types [3] be treated in a reasonable way. In the last few decades an immense literature has accumulated on the subject, and certainly there are groups of individuals who are so similar with respect to some traits, and so different from other individuals, that it seems very reasonable to consider them as belonging together to a special class, as being a type.

In accordance with differing approaches toward the understanding of human behavior, attempts have been made to define these groups in various ways.

Plato's metaphysical division of the human soul into three parts we meet again in Bain's classification of men as "mentals," "men of action," and "vitals." The theoretical, economic, social, and political types of Spranger represent the expression of another still more philosophical approach. Physical features form the basis for the creation of anthropological types marked by differences of skull, hair, color, and so on. Impressed by differences in temperament or, more recently, by differences in the functions of the endocrine glands, some investigators have distinguished the melancholic, the choleric, the phlegmatic, and the sanguine types. An interest in the constitutional habit was the basis for the well-known types of Kretschmer which have achieved significance in psychiatry. From the psychological standpoint, types have been discriminated on the basis of the special development of single senses (the auditive type, the visual type, etc.). Finally there should be mentioned the much-discussed distinction of types according to differences in the individual's general attitude to the world, the introverted and extroverted types.

In all these hypotheses there is certainly something which we feel to be true. Notwithstanding this, all these attempts must be considered failures, even if they happen to be useful for some practical purpose. The never-ending discussion about the correctness of these distinctions shows this only too clearly. The cause of the failure seems to me to be grounded in the same methodological error as the failure of the reflex theory. Single phenomena are taken as essential factors either because of their accidentally coming into the foreground or because of theoretical prejudice. If one considers such single factors as the basis of personality, then one easily yields to the impression that individuals are merely examples of types characterized by these factors. This procedure is wrong, however, in its selection of the determining factors, and does injustice to the nature of individuality. The error in selection could be avoided if the factors were determined by the methods we used in establishing the preferred behavior of the individual. And such a procedure alone would do justice to the nature of individuality. Under these circumstances individuals would never appear as mere examples of types. We could, of course, use the concept of types as a means of sorting the immense variety of individuals for practical purposes. Then it might be useful in several respects. It might serve to reveal the significance of some attributes within the organization of an individual, to reveal the special character which an individual may have through the predominance of such an attribute. Further, the better knowledge of similarities and differences in individuals might help us to understand why some are fitted to get along with one another, others not. Finally, the concept of types, which has frequently been utilized for stressing differences between groups, might be extremely useful in demonstrating factors of similarity.

In connection with the question of the functional

relation between those factors of personality which we call preferred, I should like to suggest that factor analysis might offer an appropriate method of approach. Factor analysis tries to discover the factors on the basis of which personality can be understood. If it were possible to determine with this instrument the performances that are preferred (in the sense in which we have defined the term), then we might hope to discover by objective mathematical methods some consistent traits of personality. But this cannot be attained through a comparative investigation of a great number of subjects by means of standardized tests. How can we tell whether we grasp the essential factors with these tests? Methodologically this would be possible only if we could study the tested group under conditions which represent an ordered state for each individual within the group. This presupposes, however, that we are acquainted with the nature of each person in that group; and so we are brought back to the individual as our point of departure. Factor analysis may have value as a technique if it is applied fruitfully to the individual proper, where the major determinants of preferred performances and their structural interrelation within the whole personality may become susceptible of mathematical representation.

The methods which till now we have considered instrumental for determining the basic constants of an individual are more or less confined to a cross-sectional aspect of his *present* behavioral state, but there can be no doubt that we ought to include the temporal aspect of his total behavior — that is, the course of life and the biographical span of the personality explored. In other words, the biographical method or "anamnesis," as we call it in medicine, is an indispensable supplementary source of information. It can furnish a distinction between the factors which make for ordered or disordered behavior, between genuine constants and the more casual phenotypic reaction patterns, habits, and so on. Only on the basis of information regarding the course of the individual's life can we really identify unequivocally the constants in question, by recognizing their consistency and persistence in the pattern of that person's development.

I am, of course, well aware of a question which probably has beset the mind of the reader since I began to outline the importance of preferred behavior. In what way are the individual's constants influenced and modified by *experience*, and in what way do they in turn shape and mold the experiences of the individual? In attempting to answer this question, we must first of all recognize the ultimate consequence which follows from the conception of preferred behavior. If there are any constants at all, then they must operate as selective and accentuating factors upon the experiences of the individual and the stimuli by which he is affected.

In order to appreciate this rule we must recall the result of our discussion of the problem of drives. It will be remembered that we came to the conclusion that the only drive or basic tendency of the organism is to actualize itself according to its potentialities in the highest possible degree. This is possible only if the organism is faced with situations it can cope with. From what we have learned about the behavior of our patients we know that, if the patient is faced with environmental conditions with which his changed personality cannot come to terms, then he is either not touched at all or he responds with a catastrophic reaction. He can exist — that is, actualize his capacities — only if he finds a new milieu that is appropriate to his capacities. Only then can he act in an orderly way, and only then can his powers of recognition, attention, memory, and learning be at their best.

These facts offer us the key to our question regarding the relation between preferred performances and experience in the normal person. The experiences a person has, or is able to assimilate or acquire, hinge upon his capacities, and these we can infer from his preferred ways of behavior. Only if given the opportunity to realize himself in these ways will he be in an ordered state, which is the basis of good performance; in other words, the more the demands made upon him correspond to his preferred ways of behaving, the more nearly perfect will his achievements be. Of course, these preferred ways of behaving have a determinable range of variation and should not be treated as fixed and rigid patterns. The ex-

perienceable environmental segments may vary
within certain limits according to this range of variability. And it is this scale of variability which has
to be carefully studied and weighed by the investi-
gator of the mutual interdependence of preferred
behavior and environmental demands. In order to
determine and secure the best possible performances
of an individual, and in order to develop his manifold
potentialities to their full capacity, we have to know
the extent of this interdependence. In pathology this
fact is quite obvious. We have acquainted ourselves
with the rule that patients have catastrophic reactions, and that their intact performance fields are also
reduced, if the demands of the outer world exceed
the scope of their impaired capacities. Such a dimi-
nution of capacity for performance also takes place
if the demands are too low, and the capacities which
remain are not called upon and utilized to their full
extent. Then a shrinkage of the patient's milieu and
personality sets in which is greater than the actual
impairment would entail.

From this it follows that, if we wish to prompt the
development of an organism in the way best suited
to its potentialities, our demands must be neither too
low nor too high. The measure of the commensurate
degree is to be found in the organism's range of preferred ways of behaving.

We have tried to qualify the relation between the
demands of the outer world and the development of
the capacities of an individual. With this in mind we

can also understand the far-reaching influence of a given milieu upon the actualization of the individual's potentialities. Wherever a person grows up, his environment is of a specific nature, and this provides the cultural and social contents of his developmental socialization; that is, the determination of the specific character of the potentialities of any individual is oriented by the contents of his milieu. This relation between the individual and his environment has implications for a number of much-discussed problems, such, for instance, as questions having to do with learning and education, with racial differences, and with differences in the development of societies and culture. These problems seem to pertain to quite diverse topics, but in my opinion they all go back ultimately to one question — namely, how can the individual actualize himself in the world in the way that best corresponds to his capacities?

I should like to comment briefly on my views on the solution of the problem of differences in character between the inhabitants of different countries and states and between races.[4] These differences stand out most strikingly if, under the influence of a bias, we push single properties into the foreground as chief characteristics and compare the groups or races as to such properties. If we do this, we see only the differences and are inclined to overrate them in a way that does not at all correspond to the facts. This fallacious procedure is the mainspring of all personal national and racial prejudice and one of the chief causes of much of the suffering and distress in the world. Fundamentally this state of affairs is the result of a lack or a falsification of knowledge, and of a corruption of science, which lends pseudo-scientific arguments and pretended justification to all kinds of abominable actions.

The importance of enlightenment in this field cannot be overstated. It cannot be said often enough that individuals, peoples, races, can actualize themselves without harming each other, that this can be accomplished only by an adequate organization of group life, and that, moreover, the life of any group is guaranteed only in an organization which guarantees the existence of other groups as well. The search for innate factors of any kind which can account for racial differences has been vain, and it is not surprising that this is so. The empirical evidence adduced and the painstaking analysis undertaken by Boas, Klineberg, and others, have shown that all the varieties of race and culture which have been attributed to inborn, unchangeable factors are as a matter of fact culturally and socially determined. Even such differences as those in pigmentation and other constitutional properties do not alter the fact that all men are endowed with equal inherent potentialities. All individual differences granted — and, in fact, precisely because of the vast variety of existing individual differences — we know that no race possesses traits by which it can be distinguished intrinsically from other races. The fact that there is great diversity of traits of personality in all races and groups, and that it traverses the boundaries of every population and sector of the globe, proves that all the phenomena which are common to a group or race are not reducible to common inborn personality traits in that group.

Our biological point of view, especially our notion of preferred behavior, would seem to contradict these statements. Therefore I must reëmphasize the postulate that the range of variability in the preferred ways of human behavior has to be considered as the deciding factor in the variety of social and cultural patterns. Within the interactional relation of environment and organism the members of any group will actualize their potentialities according to the peculiarities of their environment, adapting themselves to its natural and social demands. The problem of differences in society and culture is basically similar to the problem of personality, as far as the contents of life, conflicts and demands, are concerned. Here, too, we cannot draw artificial dividing lines in the true unitary pattern of life in which the person and his environment are interwoven, and we have therefore to reject the doctrines of the extreme environmentalist, as well as those of the extreme believer in heredity. How the relation between individual and society presents itself from our standpoint we shall see later.

On the basis of the relationship we have tried to establish between the range of variability in preferred behavior and the diversity of cultural products, we come to noteworthy conclusions. (1) Our assertion that man as a species is endowed with potentialities which are basically equal is confirmed by the fact that, different from ours as modes of life and thought among primitive peoples are, there is no doubt in the minds of competent anthropologists that, if we transplant a member of such a group into our society, he can be trained to think in our terms; this holds particularly, of course, with regard to children. (2) The importance of the relationship between capacities and environment for ordered behavior may again be ascertained by the study of abnormal persons. In contrast with normal persons, they are so rigidly bound to a definite environment that they perish if this environmental setting is changed in a way not adequate to their preserved potentialities. This pathological fact teaches us something with regard to the adjustment of the normal person to changes of environment. The variability of which we have spoken has a certain limit. If the changes imposed upon an individual or group go beyond the limits of possible adjustmental variations, or if, in other words, the demands of the outer world exceed the range of adequacy for the individual, then catastrophe occurs and the organism can no longer function in orderly fashion. I think this rule may offer us a key to the understanding of certain disorders in individual behavior as well as in the functioning of a society. For example, many a disturbance has been found in the development of children who are left-handed, and who have been forced into right-handedness, in which the disorder appears in fields totally different from the sphere of left- or right-handedness, so that only a scrutinizing analysis can reveal the cause. Later we shall discuss certain consequences of this rule for social life. (3) There is a third aspect in the relation of preferred behavior and environment. It will be recalled that when we turned our attention to the problem of how experience influences preferred behavior, and vice versa, we stressed the fact that the preferred tendencies of an individual operate as selective and accentuating factors upon his experience. It may not seem obvious, but close reflection suggests that there is an intimate relation between the preferred modes of behavior of the individual and the psychological motivations of his conduct, contact with others, likes and dislikes, and attitudes toward life.

Just as we have agreed with Woodworth that habits once formed may achieve a motivational impulse, so we may assume that the drive to actualize one's potentialities also operates as a motivating force in one's emotional valuations in accordance with one's preferred ways of acting.

VIII

THE INDIVIDUAL AND OTHERS

WE HAVE elaborated the contention that there is only one motive by which human activity is set going: the tendency to actualize oneself. This emphasis upon the supreme importance of the nature of the individual might easily lead to an interpretation of our standpoint as an asocial individualism and egotism. In fact, however, such an interpretation is flatly opposed to the idea of human nature which we are attempting to advance. It is directly opposed to the fact that individuality never means simply "I am" but always that simultaneously with me there exist other creatures.

Our observation of our patients shows that they cannot actualize themselves without respect to their surroundings in some degree, especially to other persons. The sick man is exposed to catastrophic reactions to a higher degree than the normal man; he can perform only if he finds a milieu which allows him to avoid catastrophic reactions. This implies that his behavior has to presume definite environmental conditions, in particular the existence of other men. The patient must develop an adjustment to others and limit himself according to the social actuality of others.

True, as we have said before, the patient is subject to this connection with others in a somewhat passive way. Even on this reduced level, however, such a connection indicates that the existence of one man presupposes another man. Because of their lack of the capacity for abstraction, our patients are not capable of creating contacts actively and spontaneously. Therefore their existence depends to a high degree upon the coöperative activity of their fellow men. One can hardly find a better example of the fact that the attitude of self-restriction belongs to natural human behavior than that given by the behavior of normal persons toward the sick, which is characterized by active self-restriction in the interest of the sick. This fact gains greater significance in view of the contrasting behavior of our patients, who lack the capacity for voluntary self-restriction. It is because of this that they seem so self-centered and that they are unable to build up by themselves a real community or a social world. What patients exhibit of an apparent social character is actually something quite different.

The attitude of self-restriction in the normal person has often been considered to be caused by the impact of extraneous forces, and understood, like other altruistic customs, as a mechanism for yielding to insuperable forces in the struggle of life. In this sense all social norms are supposed to be merely the products of sublimation. We have explained, however, that such an interpretation is incompatible with the facts. Self-restricting behavior can be understood only if we assume that it is due to an underlying tendency which belongs to human nature, or that, as John Dewey says, "the ideas involved in such behavior appeal to something in human nature and awaken in [man] an active response." Otherwise there would be only a struggle of all against all, a condition out of which *social* life could never originate; the law of the jungle would prevail.

Self-restriction in the interest of another, however, is not the only form of behavior which reveals that a connection with and dependence upon others is part of the nature of man, and even requisite for the existence of the individual. There is still another behavioral interrelation between individuals which is inherent in man. The self-actualization of the individual in his social environment can take place only by his encroaching upon another's freedom, by claiming something from another, by imposing upon another to a certain degree. The primary fact that the individual does not exist alone, but with other creatures, necessarily implies the incomplete realization of every individual's nature; it entails impact, antagonism, conflict and competition with others.

Self-actualization on the part of one individual can be attained only by some renunciation on the part of another, and each must ask from others that renunciation. Hence there is not a preestablished harmony between human beings. According to the myth of the expulsion from Paradise, man lost that state of permanent mutual accord through the sin of cognition. No longer is it possible for him to realize himself through a coming to terms, without conflict, with his natural and social environment. Neither offers him the immediate primeval adequacy that Paradise seems to have offered. Man can no longer live in effortless harmony with the world. He has to seek it in an active way. And he is free to make his own decisions.

One might evaluate this freedom as essentially positive or essentially negative; certainly it remains a basic characteristic of human nature, as we can demonstrate clearly in the changes in our patients. Being individual, being free, implies the necessity of encroaching upon the freedom of others. The two things are the same. Therefore, we may say that the activity of encroaching also belongs to the nature of man.

These two kinds of behavior, self-restriction and encroachment, have been spoken of (by McDougall,[1] for example), under the names of "submission" and "aggression," as two basic drives of human nature. In terms of our general criticism of the theory of drives and instincts we have no reason to assume such inherent drives. These two types of behavior are not separate and antagonistic tendencies operating in the human being. Man is neither aggressive nor submissive by nature. He is driven to actualize himself and to come to terms with his environment. In doing so, he has at times to be submissive and at times to be aggressive, depending on the situation.

Whenever either form of behavior achieves dominance in such a way that all the activities of the individual seem to be under its control, then something has gone wrong in the relationship between the individual and the surrounding world. Either the individual lacks adequate centering or the demands arising from the world are so difficult that he is not able to cope with them. Under such conditions one or the other of these two types of behavior comes abnormally to the foreground, and, according to the law of isolation, behavior takes on an abnormal character. Then we encounter either self-sacrifice or aggressiveness. Abnormal aggressiveness or submissiveness we observe especially in patients who lack the capacity for abstraction and in those in whom there is a pathological isolation of certain personality sectors. In the latter case the individual may be driven by an irresistible urge to fulfill the needs — say abnormal hunger or sexual desire — that result from this isolation. Then he is inconsiderate, reckless, and highly aggressive in seeking the release of this urge. This can be observed in patients with organic as well as functional diseases. Thus we find aggression as a characteristic symptom of neurosis. Abnormal aggression is always combined with abnormal sub-

mission, however, and what we observe in our
patients is an abnormal exaggeration of normal
behavior. Normally behavior fluctuates in adequate
proportions between self-restriction and an encroachment upon the freedom of others. The
exaggeration in pathology is the sequel of a lack
of proper centering, which, as we have explained,
always produces opposed reactions that alternate
abnormally. As in normal persons, the situation
determines which type of behavior becomes the
figure, comes to the foreground; the only difference
is that the intensity is abnormally exaggerated. That
behavior always appears by which in a given condition the organism can best come to terms with the
outer world; and this rule holds for a changed
personality as well as a normal one.

Aggressiveness may come into the foreground if
an individual is afraid to show his inclination to
submissiveness, because he fears that people would
misuse his subjection and that he would meet with
situations that he could not bear. On the other
hand, abnormal submission may appear as an
expression of "repressed" normal aggression.[2] A
child may have grown up under conditions in which
he faced the danger of unreasonable punishment
for any attempt at encroaching upon other people,
especially his mother — and that even if the degree
of the intrusion was normal for a child of that age.
One of my patients found that any opposition to
her mother made her lose her mother's affection,

and without this she could not live. This led her to suppress all resistance, and eventually she was governed by abnormal submission. This experience influenced her behavior during her entire future life. As an adult, she seemed to be very compliant and gave the impression of being an abnormally submissive person. In certain situations, however, abnormally aggressive behavior suddenly appeared, astonishing not only the people around her but also the patient herself. As a matter of fact, such a person is not abnormally submissive, as it would appear to a superficial view, but *ambivalent*; from this ambivalence emerges abnormal submissiveness as well as abnormal aggressiveness.

Normal, ordered life asks for a balanced relation between compliant and encroaching behavior. Only then can the individual realize himself, and assist others in their self-realization. Furthermore, the highest forms of human relationship, such as love and friendship, are dependent on the individual's ability and opportunity to realize both these aspects of human behavior. This is evident so far as self-restriction is concerned, but encroachment also belongs to every relationship between individuals. Love is not merely a mutual gratification and compliance; it is a higher form of self-actualization, a challenge to develop both oneself and another in this respect. This challenge involves aggression inasmuch as it involves influencing — perhaps even coercing — another to do things which sometimes seem foreign to him. Self-restriction is experienced as inherent in human nature; it corresponds to what we call the ethical, to the norms. Our intrusion upon others is often experienced as a suffering that has to be endured, as one of the difficulties of life that must be borne. It is experienced as suffering because interference with one's own freedom or that of others has the appearance of injustice. But if one understands the necessity of such interference for one's own or another's sake, one can tolerate or enact it without self-accusation, and with less harm to others.

If this conception of the relationship between one individual and another fits the facts, if all relations between individuals are determined by the tendency of each to realize himself, then we may draw the general conclusion that the individual is primary in all social organization. Very often the "we"— that is, the relationship between the individual and others — is considered the primary factor, and the individual's behavior is supposed to be understandable only in terms of that "we." [3] Indeed, there is no question that in a concrete situation it is often the case that the individual is determined to a high degree by the community in which he lives. But the question is: Is this a normal situation — that is, does it correspond to the nature of man, or is it merely an accidental phenomenon? In other words, is the "we" empirically given? Can it serve to make understandable in terms of human nature the self-realization of the individual? Is the fact that the "we" determines the behavior of the individual sufficient to prove that it is normal? There is no doubt that its empirical character is not necessarily a sign that we are dealing with a normal phenomenon. We know many such "we's" which can easily be proved not to be of a normal character. To appreciate the connection between the "we" and the individual we must take into consideration the phenomena of the "we" which in their very nature guarantee the existence of the individual.

Even to raise the question in this way may seem to be unjustified, however, since nature may have no interest in the individual, but only in the group, the species, the race — in short, in the "we." The widespread assumption, in fact, is that nature is not interested in the individual. It is supposed to be wasteful of individuals, to have no other goal than the perpetuation of the species. General as it is, this assumption is in no way based on facts. Everywhere in nature we meet with individuals, not only in the realm of man but also in that of animals and plants. What we call kinds, races, and so on, are products of human thought in its generalizing aspect. And what appears to occur irrespective of individuals and as a waste of individuals can also be understood as a consequence of the imperfection of the single individual in a situation in which immense numbers of individuals coexist. How are we to understand the immense variety of forms, colors, and ways of living, without assuming that they are all of importance to nature, an importance which is much greater than it usually appears to the human mind to be, especially in the scientific approach? On principle the scientific approach abstracts from particulars and takes into consideration only what can be described in general terms. This is a procedure leading to negative statements not in accordance with nature. We shall stress later the fact that there is nothing negative in nature. Nature is always positive. Does it not follow that the present is the center of importance? And is the present not always individual? What we call a "species" is never present; it belongs to the past or to the future. Only the individual is present. Is not such an abstraction as species a special expression of human thinking, which alone can grasp the negative, and with that the past and the future? Let us remember in this connection that the patients we have been describing are unable to grasp the negative and the general, and unable, as well, to grasp the past and the future. They live in one dimension, in the concrete. We have traced this back to the impairment of the capacity for abstraction. Nature in general seems to live in only one dimension (the present), the dimension of the concrete, of the individual. Only the human being, and possibly some of the higher animals, goes beyond this dimension.

My assumption that nature is concerned with the individual may appear to be merely a metaphysical belief. Yet it is certainly no more metaphysical than the idea which ascribes to nature a lack of concern with the individual and sees as its goal the preservation of the species.

From this point of view, not all "we" phenomena are real, but only those which guarantee the realization of the individual. All other concepts of the relationship between the individual and other individuals represent accidental connections related to a variety of factors, such as the concept of reflexes or of "higher centers," all of which are more or less inadequate.

If we consider the "we" as secondary to the individual, the "we" should by no means be thought of simply as an extraneous and secondary connection between individuals. It is not simply a sum made up of individuals. Real group life, social life, is not an accidental living-together, nor is it based on a voluntary "social contract." A concrete group life may develop in the first way, if individuals happen to live together under equal conditions and feel impelled to help each other against common difficulties. Yet real social life, whether under these conditions or under those in which a social unit is constructed by means of a "contract," will develop only if some genuine communion between its members exists. If this is not the case, the whole structure is shaken when conditions change. The political disasters of recent decades in Europe make an excellent case to illustrate the instability and insecurity of units built up on the basis of external connections between men.

The collapse of such social entities is caused by the incapacity of the "we" in question to guarantee natural ways of existence for individuals. The only "we" that is real and "natural," and constitutes a true social organization, is one which can do this. This shows that the "we" is determinable only through the individual, that he is actually the measure of its suitability, that it is secondary to him. Where it asserts its primacy, the existence not only of the individual but of the "we" is endangered. If the state pretends an inherent value independent of the rights of individuals (to take only one example), restriction of human nature takes place, with serious consequences to the existence of both individuals and state.

This explanation contains implicitly a criticism of all forms of collectivism. The term "collectivism" may mean a rational organization of society or a metaphysic entity as a thing in itself. In the first case, every endeavor to build a collective presupposes a certain idea for the manner of its organization. Collectivism per se cannot represent a goal. Every collectivistic endeavor uses collectivism as a means — not always expressed but always intended — for the realization of the best manner of existence for the individuals in the collective. Only if this is guaranteed does the collective have sense and will it have permanency. An organization which is unable to guarantee this is not a true collective. This collectivistic endeavor can be directed toward different ends, according to the idea one has of the nature of man. If one considers freedom as essential to human beings, any collectivistic organization is wrong — i.e., contradicts itself — which is not constructed in such a way that the freedom of all individuals is guaranteed.

If collectivism is regarded as a hypostasized reality in the metaphysical or naturalistic sense, then any organization which matches the conception of this reality fits the purpose. The organization does not have to concern itself primarily with the individual. However, collectivism on such a basis, whether in theory or in practice, is subject to the same criticism as any metaphysical or naturalistic dogma. It opposes the conception of man which considers freedom essential. The term "freedom" does not mean the arbitrary right of each individual to do what he likes — *laissez-faire, laissez-aller.* On the contrary, it means the right and the inner necessity to actualize oneself, a right which, as we have seen, presupposes the possibility of actualization on the part of all other individuals. For freedom fundamentally presupposes the freedom of all others — equality; not, indeed, equality in the simple political sense of the word, but equal rights and equal duties. The restriction of the personality involved in the latter must be considered a limitation caused by the living together of individuals under certain conditions, not as determined by any metaphysical or natural law. Progress means the amelioration of these conditions to allow for a more and more adequate self-realization on the part of all individuals. The fact that a certain degree of restriction will probably always remain is a consequence of individuality, i.e., of the coexistence of individuals.

As we have said, the individual is not independent of the "we." Yet he cannot exist without the "we"; he can realize his nature only within the group. The individual and the "we" depend upon each other.

Even though the individual is primary to society, without question he is influenced to a very high degree by society. His life is determined by the habits, customs, and institutions characteristic of the society he lives in. The problem is how these habits and customs develop. It has sometimes been assumed that they emerge simply from the fact that this kind of association of beings exists, that they are products of a collective mind. From our point of view self-restriction and encroachment upon the freedom of others are the two basic aspects of all forms of living together, and, with that, of all social organization; they are not simply the mechanically conditioned products of a society that preëxists or takes primacy over individuals; rather, they emerge during the building up and constituting of a society. They are the avenues for the best possible self-actualization of all individuals forming that society, and by virtue of this they are instruments for the creation of the best possible society. It is true that there are ideas which are common to a group — and they are often much more fixed and influential than the ideas of individuals — but they are the products of the minds of individuals. They originate within society, and the actual living together of individuals is a very important cause of their development, but they are built up, or at least accepted and transformed, by individuals.

In this respect our concept is very close to the rule of the convergence of internal and external factors which the late William Stern introduced into psychology. It seems to me that modern anthropology and social psychology have adduced sufficient evidence of this interaction or convergence. It is scarcely necessary to support this statement by recalling the variability of the I.Q. according to modifications in milieu. In his book, *Experimental Social Psychology*, Gardner Murphy has summarized the results of pertinent investigations in the statement that the I.Q. in the same children or in different children with equal endowments varies essentially according to environment. The dependence of the I.Q. to a very large degree upon environmental conditions has also been ascertained by Otto Klineberg in comparative investigations dealing with negroes and with rural and urban population. Recent investigations in Iowa have even led to the assertion that the I.Q.'s of feeble-minded children can be markedly improved by changes in environment. Perhaps the most striking illustration of the way in which this convergence operates is offered by the analysis of language, as, for instance, the naming of objects. From the linguistic studies of Wilhelm von Humboldt and of Ernst Cassirer,[4] and from the psychopathology of aphasia, we know that the function of naming objects does not represent a simple superficial connection between a thing and a word. We know that language is more than a mere reflection of outside objects in the mind, that it is rather a means in itself for building up the world in a particular way — that is, in a categorical way. The categorical, or abstract, attitude is a capacity belonging to every human being and endows him with the ability to vary his perspective and to orient his conception of the world by a variety of frames of reference. If the language of civilized people differs from that of primitive ones, the reason lies not in differences in capacities but in differences in the use of the same capacities according to different environmental requirements.

We have already explained the role of the abstract attitude in the process of building habits.* It plays a similar role in the building up of customs and institutions. Customs are built up in a historical development that covers thousands of years; they are transmitted from generation to generation,

* See p. 135.

modified and changed by our ancestors and by our fellow human beings of the present.

To a great extent this transmission and acceptance of customs takes place during infancy and youth, and rather passively. In the adult, however, customs which are actually followed are integrated with the personality by the capacity for assuming the abstract attitude. As we have explained, conditioned responses are established in early youth; it is not until they are transformed into genuine performances that they become the habits of the adult, and this in turn is possible only by virtue of the abstract attitude. The same is the case with the customs which are taken over by the individual. They can never become established without the abstract attitude, and it is responsible for the fact that an association between a definite stimulus and an act (whether accidental in origin or imposed by outer circumstance) becomes a true custom. For a custom is never an external phenomenon, but is connected with the whole personality. Without the abstract attitude — that is, insight into the significance of customs for the life of the individual and society — its development is impossible. This attitude is a prerequisite for the taking over of a custom and is particularly important for the modification of customs according to new conditions, which is indispensable to a living culture, since without this continual change there would be standstill and decay.[5]

Persons with brain injuries demonstrate all this clearly. The customs they follow are those of their pre-morbid stage. They are unable to change these; on the contrary, they have abnormally rigid and fixed habitual modes of social behavior. As we have explained, they are able to find new adaptations and establish new habits only with the help of their healthy fellow men. And the adaptations acquired by this procedure are so connected with specific situations and correspond so closely to the particular organization of the patient's personality that they are unsuited to become the customs of a group. As a result of the homogeneity of environment in which patients live in a hospital, similar habits may originate in individuals, but never customs that are common to a group. And only this is characteristic of social habits.

In short, such living together is not real social life. Consequently, these similar habits are very easily disturbed. Since the patients lack adequate centering and are very susceptible to immediate stimuli, they are always ready to react even to minute changes in their surroundings in a way that is not consistent with these habits.

Thus we come to the conclusion that customs originate in society, but that their origin, still more their transmission, depends upon the abstract attitude on the part of the individuals concerned. They are accepted as belonging to the personality and are changed according to the needs of the situation by means of the abstract attitude. The faculty of transmitting customs as such belongs only to human beings. It is never observed in animals. It is true that one occasionally finds traits which might be called cultural, like the domestication of plants and the division of labor in some species of insects, but these traits are not acquired by any individual creature; they belong to the structural pattern of its species and therefore cannot be changed. Man has to acquire such customs all over again with each generation; only the capacity for transmission is inherited. Ruth Benedict says very correctly that "man is the culture-making animal." I should like to add that this faculty is an expression of his ability to grasp the abstract.

The development of an institution can be much more readily observed than that of a custom because it is built up before our eyes. There is no question that institutions originate as the result of reasonable deliberation in which the whole group participates more or less. The individual, being a member of the group, acknowledges them.

To sum up, a habit is a means of adaptation on the part of the individual to the conditions of the nonhuman environment; habits help particularly to guarantee one's physical existence. A custom is a means of adaptation to the general conditions of life in a *group*. An institution is an adaptive measure that has to do with the socio-economic conditions of a group. Common to all these adaptive forms is the fact that, once built up, they can function without continual voluntary acts on the part of the individual. They achieve a certain independence of the individual. The formation of habits calls for very little volitional participation on the part of the individual; that of institutions calls for much. For this reason institutions vary greatly, and it is easy to misuse them. From all these adaptive processes there emerges a strong impulse toward action. They become valuable aids in the accomplishments of individuals and make the self-actualization of the organism easier; there is therefore a strong urge to preserve them.

In the course of history many of the habits, customs, and institutions in civilization and culture have attained a certain emancipation from their original meaning, and thus govern human behavior without our being aware of their original purpose. In spite of the unjustified tyranny they may exercise and the obstacles they may offer to free development, they are maintained as long as they are to some degree embedded within the purposive setting of the social framework in which they play a part. If, however, this lack of relation reaches such a degree that the rules of conduct are practically detached from the real needs of a majority of the group, we are dealing with abnormal conditions. Limitations may then be imposed upon the life of the individual in such a way that sufficient leeway for self-realization is no longer conceded.

The consequences of such a condition are cata-
stropic reactions and anxiety, which the individual
tries to overcome through attacks on customs and institutions, on the government which attempts to
preserve those institutions. If it is extensive enough,
the confusion which arises from such a condition can
be used by a minority to claim spuriously, in the
name of society, the right to take over all power in
order to protect society. If such a group is victorious,
tyranny develops. Thus society comes to be divided
into groups that rule and groups that are ruled in
opposition to their own wishes, a state of affairs which
is incompatible with the essential character of human
nature because it contradicts freedom.

The members of such a society are rather like the
patient who lacks the ability to abstract and who
thus becomes the victim of an abnormal response to
outside stimuli. Like the sick person, they suffer from
the limitation of their freedom and from anxiety, with
its consequences (the shrinkage of the environment,
dependence upon and submission to other people).
And all this occurs under the necessity for maintaining physical and mental existence in some, even
the most primitive, form. Such disturbances affect
both the individual and society as long as an inadequate relationship between the two, manifested
in the abnormally exaggerated power of certain institutions, prevails. Society is then in danger of being
distorted into forms of organization which, the ruling
minority to the contrary notwithstanding, do not

correspond to the nature of man. Irrational factors are thrust into the foreground by the minority in order to make acceptable and understandable an organization which is not understandable by reason as such, because it is not adequate to human nature. Such a society is not really productive; and it is very insecure. Immense activity must be called into play to maintain the organization itself; because it has no stability within, it can be upheld only by the utilization of all the worst traits of human nature, by mechanical means, by force, by the state of anxiety which tyrannical rulers, as we have explained, often produce intentionally as a means of tuning the spirit of the masses to one key and level of action. An external order only hides the disorder which exists below the surface, splendid as that surface sometimes is.

Such a pseudo-social organization may be compared with an organism in disease, and we may speak of such a society as sick. Normal society means a type of organization through which the fullest possible actualization on the part of all individuals is assured. This presupposes the possibility that both aspects of human nature, self-restriction and encroachment, can be effective in a balanced fashion. The attempt to build up social life based on the notion of a drive to submission or to aggression, or of an antagonistic struggle between the two, is futile. If we acknowledge and utilize social organization as an instrument by means of which all individuals may actualize themselves to an optimal degree, then a genuine social life becomes possible. Only under these conditions is a social organization capable of doing justice to every individual; only this makes it a real social organization and secures its duration. Far as we may be from realizing such a society nowadays, it seems to me extremely important to be aware of the fundamentals on which its possibility is grounded. Only in this way can we discover the concrete causes of failure in a given situation and the appropriate ways to correct the failure.

Failure, or a series of failures, may be the consequence of a wrong procedure in the realization of a sound idea; it does not necessarily speak against the correctness of that idea itself. In the same way, success, taken as the sole measure, does not speak for the correctness of the underlying idea; only success in accordance with the essence of human nature constitutes a real success. And the basic reason for failure in this respect, it seems to me, lies in the misinterpretation of human nature. Ultimately all failures in social organization are caused by an underestimation of the significance of the abstract attitude and by a misjudgment of the detrimental influence which can emanate from human traits if one changes them through artificial isolation. With the help of the abstract attitude the fallacy which is basic to all false social organization can be disclosed.

THE FALLACY OF "ISOLATION" IN SOCIAL PHILOSOPHY

IF ONE ranges the facts of history against the assertion that man's capacity for abstract behavior, for freedom and self-restriction, has paramount significance for the organization of social life, and if in particular one considers the present world situation, the idea may seem quite wrong, not to say ridiculous. If the capacity for abstract behavior were really the highest attribute of human nature, why, one may ask, are human beings not able to build up a social organization that will guarantee human existence at least to some degree? How is it possible that human ingenuity should be used essentially for the purpose of destruction? How is it possible that hatred and vandalism should govern the world to such an extent not only that the civilization of western Europe is in danger of being wiped out, but that human existence in its widest expansion seems to be menaced by a struggle of all against all? How is all this possible in view of the fact that we possess the capacity of reasoning?

Such an objection indicates a failure to understand the dialectic procedure of cognition. Erroneously, it considers as ends conditions which repre-

sent only transitory states in the process of the
human being's coming to terms with the world. In
our discussion of acquiring such a simple skill as
bicycling, it was shown that many wrong actions are
necessary before the situation which makes the correct performance possible is found. As we have
demonstrated, all misinterpretation of the phenomena
of life originates in the application of the analytic
method; we can attain adequate results only by a
special type of cognition, an activity that transcends
this analytic procedure. We have to admit, however,
that this method in itself contains the danger of
error. If it is so difficult to find the procedure through
which bicycling — such a simple form of coming to
terms with the world! — becomes possible, how
much more difficult it is to find an adequate way for
a large group of human beings to live together, not
to mention mankind.

The dialectic point of view will prevent us from
considering any given state of affairs as a permanent
one and as the sole expression of what the human
being is capable of in principle. We will be mindful
of the fact that we are always dealing with partitive
results, which we are not allowed to take for granted
as absolutes. Every historical event, as it goes into
the mere factual record, shows definitely the characteristics of a process in isolation; it is a more or less
successful attempt to actualize human beings with
the help of society. The more it thrusts into the
foreground single tendencies of men, the more it

demands its own recognition as an absolute and emancipated value, the less successful it is. The social order which then develops is not adequate for a great number of its members. Because its isolation and exaggeration of one normal trait, aggressiveness, it is neither productive nor secure, a caricature of real society.

Our methodological point of view will lead us to avoid the fallacy of overestimating a temporary and incidental condition. We shall not forget the needs of the true nature of man. We shall not let ourselves be deceived by false idols, nor commit suicide by following blindfold the tendencies and orders of a tyranny which denies human nature. On the other hand, we shall be capable of avoiding the attitude of hopeless skepticism into which so many are driven in the present situation.

My predecessor in these lectures, Étienne Gilson, has said very truly, "In philosophy skepticism is defeatism." [1] To this I should like to add that the statement applies not only to philosophy but to all knowledge and action. Skepticism is not in accord with the phenomenon of life. Life is always positive. Only human thought, through the isolating method, produces the negative. Everybody who has to do with living beings, especially with human beings, knows that in practice negative procedure can play a merely transient role and that it is fruitful only in relation to positive measures. This concerns the educator as well as the physician. And it refutes skepticism in principle.

Closer consideration reveals that the skeptical standpoint is always a subterfuge, as Max Horkheimer,[2] in particular, has pointed out. Even when it appears as a philosophical attitude, it is not genuine, but a secondary phenomenon, a phenomenon of escape from unbearable conditions. In his inability to realize himself, in his struggle with given conditions, the individual withdraws into himself. He is not aware of the danger involved in this mental isolation, of the shrinkage of his personality and the mental suicide which this attitude implies. It is concealed from him by a subterfuge in an individualistic ideology which glorifies the ego as part of a selected aristocratic class. His existence would be impossible without a privileged economic status, by which he is supported as the mental patient is by his fellow men. In skepticism we are dealing with a special form of the attempt to exist without taking into consideration the existence of others, with their justifiable demands. Another form is to be found in the hedonistic attitude.[3] This attitude, too, tries to avoid any participation in the difficulties and unhappiness of the life of man and confines the meaning of life to the pursuit of pleasure; it shuns grief and seeks escape in pleasure. This standpoint is close to the Freudian idea that human behavior is understandable on the basis of the pleasure principle, or, to put it in another way, that the purpose of drives is to find release from hidden urges. The hedonist tries especially to find a release from tension. I need scarcely recall our conclusion that from such a point of view normal behavior is never understandable. It is not understandable in this case because the hedonistic tendency originates in the abnormal isolation of one attribute of human nature. It is impossible in this way to achieve real self-actualization, to "live" in the true sense of the word. The hedonist may not be aware of the situation because his judgment is disturbed, especially in the abstract attitude, by the narcotization in which he lives. In consequence he is incapable of experiencing the positive character of joy; he experiences only the release from tension and the absence of pain and grief. Like Freud's concept of drives, the hedonistic way of thinking deprives the individual of the true experience of the joy and beauty of life. It can never guarantee the existence of the individual or of society; it can be held only for a time because it disintegrates the personality and with that prevents self-actualization. Enjoyment of life, happiness, and self-actualization belong together. Enjoyment of life is a special type of self-actualization, the happiness which originates in the individual's adequate coming to terms with the world. Because this scarcely ever remains constant, happiness can hold the center of the stage only for a certain time. But during the rest of the time it does not vanish; it operates in the background, giving the life of the individual the special flavor which is so characteristic of the well-adjusted person. Any attempt to secure unceasing happiness is destined to failure; where it appears as a constant phenomenon we are dealing with pathology, as, for example, in the maniac. The hedonistic attitude is a kind of withdrawal from the world, and such an attitude, whatever its cause, will never enable the individual to find an existence adequate to his nature. This holds even when the individual subjectively experiences it as moral, as, for example, in the case of Epicurus. Basically, hedonism has its origin in skepticism. In both we are dealing with the isolation of the individual from society; in both one tries to save one's own personality at any price, even the sacrifice of one's fellow beings. Both attitudes fail because they deny human nature.

Opposed to this attitude we meet another, in which the individual sacrifices himself for the sake of his fellow men. It is much more difficult to prove the ambiguity of this attitude. Some sacrifices are rightly to be considered an expression of an unusually high development of human nature. But self-sacrifice *in itself* is not of value. It is of value only if it is important for the actualization of the individual; it is of value only if the rescue of others is of such importance to the individual that his own self-realization demands this sacrifice. This is a border situation similar to one we have already discussed, in which voluntary suicide is sometimes the last way out in the attempt to preserve the personality. One has to be very careful in the evaluation of self-sacrifice, because it is often nothing more than an escape from the difficulties of normal self-actualization. If society has to ask for general self-sacrifice on the part of its members, then there is something wrong with the organization of that society. I do not mean to deny that an emergency may arise in which the individual has to sacrifice himself for the sake of society. But the individual ought always to have the possibility of making the decision for himself. Only then will the sacrifice have real value.

I am aware of the incomplete and scanty treatment I have given the problem of social organization, viewed in relation to our findings concerning the normal organism and the organism in disease. I believe, however, that the preceding discussion has prepared us sufficiently to warrant the following broader conclusion: Any attempt to determine what a normal social organization should be like is faced with the same epistemological difficulties as that of determining the characteristics of an organism.[4] Individuals are not separately existing and discrete units of the social "organism," and the latter does not constitute merely a sum total of these units. Just as the functional and material structure of an organism guarantees the normal behavior of its parts, so the organization and behavior of the social community must guarantee the existence of the individual. The study of a given social organization, like the study of an organism, has to be based upon the study of phenomena isolated by the analytic method; and we cannot proceed directly from these to a characterization of the whole which social organization represents. We are confronted once more with the limitation of the analytic method which was discussed in the first chapter.

When we deal with living beings, science of the analytic type can never speak the last word. In the last few decades it has been realized more and more that medical treatment cannot be based on science of this type alone. The same holds true for education and for practical guidance in politics. But this restriction of the value of science in no way justifies renouncing this form of cognition entirely, and surrendering to mysticism and irrational speculation. Science maintains its great value no less when we are conscious of its limits.

The analytic scientific approach remains the only one by means of which phenomena can be discovered in a systematic way. It is the only approach by means of which we can achieve that broad orbit of empirical data which renders it possible to discover which phenomena are relevant for the understanding of living beings and which not. This is its positive value. It also has great value in the negative sense, though this is often not taken into consideration with the seriousness it deserves. The unbiased registering of all phenomena which the analytic method produces necessarily brings about a critical attitude concerning the value of these phenomena for gaining a real understanding of the object in question — human nature. In the field we are interested in, this critical attitude is of the greatest importance. Science thereby reveals the danger of applying its piecemeal results to situations of inherently different structure and of making generalizations in that way. So, for example, when one makes conditioned responses the basis for understanding the natural behavior of an animal, or when one tries to explain human behavior on the basis of the results of studies of animals, or vice versa, the critical attitude reveals the error to which we have fallen victim. By scrutinizing the conditions and the consequences of isolation it can demonstrate the danger involved in this procedure, the danger of taking results obtained under these conditions as absolute. For this reason many so-called "scientific" results in the fields in question are open to a very serious criticism.

The critical attitude cautions us not to attempt an understanding of nature directly on the basis of the phenomena gained by the scientific method and refers us to the need of dialectic procedure. It reveals, further, the necessity for transcending the imminent situations of the analytic method if we wish to understand human nature and to act in its terms.

As a consequence, the personality of the scientist acquires a particular significance in relation to the task set before him. The scholar in physical science is usually confined to an elaboration of that part of the world which becomes prominent through the analytic procedure. The biologist, in addition to his consideration of physicochemical phenomena, is confronted with living beings and has to do justice to them, especially when he has to deal with men. This difference makes the actions of the physical scientist and the biologist very different.

The technologist's interference with nature means violence to nature; it is directed against the forces of nature in order to master them for the benefit of man. Even where the technologist utilizes and exploits natural energies by direct manipulation, he is able to establish and maintain his use of them only in opposition to nature, by building up protective walls against nature. Within these walls nature is not alive, but knowledge resulting from analytic procedure achieves practical utilization in the form of machines. Only when they are protected in this way against the threatening forces of nature are machines able to endure.

The biologist acts in this manner only when he is not interested in living creatures as such, as, for example, when he breeds animals for human purposes, or when his lack of knowledge prevents his real understanding of the nature of a living creature and its appropriate environment. Since biological knowledge in most cases lacks completeness, we are frequently forced to act in this way, though our goal is something quite different — that is, to provide the kind of environment which allows for the most complete realization of the nature of each creature.

This manifests itself in the activities of both the physician and the educator, which in this respect take on much the same complexion. But in education we approach still more closely the boundaries of human perfection as they are given in the imperfect knowledge of pedagogic means and ends — grounded, moreover, in man's imperfect adaptation to the world in which he has to live. Many pedagogic measures spring from the necessity of adapting the individual to the norms of the civilization and culture of which he is a part, a necessity which must be borne.[5] It is not sufficient to encourage and help the child in the development of his innate potentialities. This is the ideal of any biologically founded education, which is concerned with the development of the individual according to its nature, but the demands of civilization compel the educator to exercise, to a certain extent, mere drill; that is, to force the pupil to activities not entirely suited to his nature.

It is apparent, then, that in all scientific dealing with living beings, particularly with human beings, the personality of the scientist plays an eminent part. We should not lose sight of this fact. The biologist and the physician have to encroach upon the freedom of other human beings, and they have to do this on the basis of their own decisions. All success depends ultimately upon their personal judgment and is a matter of their own responsibility. We know that these two factors are based upon the capacity for abstraction. Thus the critical analysis of the substance of the scientific approach again discloses from another angle the significance of that capacity which our entire discourse has asserted — we think justly — to be essential to the nature of man. This analysis, on the other hand, may keep us from an overestimation of this capacity. We do not forget that in speaking of the abstract attitude we are dealing merely with a phenomenon revealed by the analytic method and that it can be evaluated only in reference to the whole organism. With this in mind, we consider other factors important for human behavior: concrete behavior and the constants that are characteristic of species and individuals. Only in a harmonious actualization of all these factors does human life appear to be normal. Whenever one of them comes abnormally to the foreground we meet with abnormal phenomena, with all the attributes of phenomena in isolation.

As we have seen, what kind of behavior, what special factor, is in the foreground depends upon the whole situation, particularly upon the environment. Thus the human being may appear in very different aspects. But human life will never be comprehensible if we take any one of these aspects as the sole characteristic of the individual or group. All misunderstandings of other individuals, all misinterpretations of the behavior of other people, are grounded basically in such a wrong procedure. For we are not dealing with individual differences in principle, but with many factors, each characteristic of all human beings, which are arranged in various ways in various individuals and groups. Thus some normal persons prefer the concrete attitude, others the abstract; in others language dominates, in still others vision. There are similar differences in peoples. The differences between primitive and civilized peoples, in particular, it becomes more and more evident, are really only variations in the arrangement of the same factors, corresponding to general differences in life and environment. Only from this standpoint, which is not only based on but enforced through a critical use of science, can one individual do justice to another, one people to another, one religion to another, one form of civilization to another. Only from this standpoint are justice and morals possible. Only from this standpoint do we achieve the humility that is in keeping with the imperfection of our coming to terms with the world. Only this attitude prevents us from taking as absolute, as *the* expression of human nature, one of those imperfect formations in which human nature appears at a given time.

We recognize further that a more nearly perfect realization can take place only through a process of mutual adaptation between peoples, which will permit a fuller actualization of all the different factors that, harmoniously combined, represent human nature. From this coöperative work nobody need be excluded except those who deliberately construct barriers and who thus decline coöperation in principle. In this latter situation we have to do with such an essential deviation from human nature that mutual understanding is impossible. We may be able to understand those who deviate in this way as anomalies, as insane or criminal, but they can never understand us and they can never become normal members of any human social organization. There is no choice for society but to protect its members against such individuals or groups. How this protection can be brought about I cannot even suggest here. I wish to stress only one fact: in our stand against these offenders of society we are not justified in doing anything which opposes human nature in principle. This would be bound to fail, because the very existence of society, which is based on human nature, would be endangered by such a procedure.

It is true that emergencies may arise to force us, in self-defense, to use methods fundamentally opposed to the needs of human nature. Otherwise we should face the danger of seeing the destruction of all that we consider essential to civilized human life, perhaps even the danger of being rooted out physically. We must never forget, however, that such situations are abnormal ones and that our actions can be justified only if they are regarded as temporary expedients. If we do, we may forfeit the very things we are seeking to defend.

In the state of despair in which so many people find themselves at present, we must always remember that we are very far from solving the problem of the adequate social organization of mankind, that we are only on the road to a goal which may be reached in the future — nobody knows when — but that we have no reason to despair if we proceed in a way determined by our knowledge of human nature.

To accept this task demands two faculties in particular: first, readiness to restrict oneself and to encroach upon others in the interest both of one's own actualization and that of others, and, second, courage in the struggle against those resistances of the inner and outer world which oppose human nature — faculties which one might consider the two paramount manifestations of the highest capacity of man, the capacity for freedom.

NOTES

NOTES

CHAPTER I

1. See C. M. CHILD, *The Physiological Foundation of Behavior* (New York, 1924); G. E. COGHILL, *Anatomy and the Problem of Behavior* (New York, 1929); C. J. HERRICK, "Anatomical Patterns," in *Physiological Zoology* (New York, 1929); K. S. LASHLEY, *Brain Mechanisms and Intelligence* (Chicago, 1929); ADOLF MEYER, "Critical Review of the Data and General Method and Deduction of Modern Neurology," *Journal of Comparative Neurology*, vol. VIII, 1898; TRIGANT BURROW, *The Biology of Human Conflict* (New York, 1938); KURT GOLDSTEIN, *The Organism* (New York, 1939).

2. See KURT GOLDSTEIN, "Die Neuroregulation," *Verhandlungen der Gesellschaft für innere Medizin und Kinderheilkunde*, vol. XLII, 1932; "Zur Frage der Restitution nach umschriebenem Hirndefect," *Schweizer Archiv für Neurologie und Psychiatrie*, vol. XIII, 1923; and *The Organism*, pp. 427 ff.

3. MAX SCHELER, *Die Stellung des Menschen im Kosmos* (Darmstadt, 1928).

4. G. W. ALLPORT, *Personality, A Psychological Interpretation* (New York, 1937).

5. See GOLDSTEIN, *The Organism*, chap. IX.

6. See GOLDSTEIN, "Zur Theorie der Funktion des Nervensystems," *Archiv für Psychiatrie*, vol. LXX, 1925, pp. 370 ff., and *The Organism*, chap. III.

7. This phenomenon, long known in psychology, falls under what is known as the Weber-Fechner law. This law says that discrimination depends upon relative rather than absolute intensities. The facts were established by E. H. Weber and G. T. Fechner more than half a century ago in investigations of perception and discrimination of weights. Weber's problem was: If we compare two weights in succession, how large must the difference in weight be to enable us to tell which is the heavier? He found that the difference which was required was not an absolute quantity but

depended upon the relation of the first weight to the second weight (a ratio of about 1 to 30 for good discrimination). Further investigations with other stimuli brought him to the general conclusion that correct comparison required a constant quantitative relationship between the two stimuli. Later Fechner, experimenting in the visual field, got similar results. In general, one can say that reactions do not increase in the same proportion as the increase of the stimuli. In order for the responses to increase in arithmetical proportion (1, 2, 3, 4, 5, 6 . . .), the corresponding stimuli must increase in geometrical proportion (2, 4, 8, 16, 32, 64 . . .). In other words, the effect of a given stimulus depends upon the condition of the organism at the moment of stimulation, upon the state of excitation at that moment (initial situation).

Closer investigations of the Weber-Fechner law have shown that it is not valid in all situations in the same way, and, what is particularly interesting for us, that the figures diverge greatly from the *theoretical expectation at extremely low and high intensities.* It is probable that in very extreme states of excitation there is a reversal of the reactions. As yet we have no systematic investigations to prove this in weight discrimination. In some somatic reactions, however, this reversal can be shown very well. The study of certain drugs, with their characteristic reactions, yields us good examples. We know that adrenalin, the extract of the adrenal gland, increases the tension of the muscles of the blood vessels, the tension of muscles of some visceral organs, such as the stomach, and so on. If one injects a small amount of this drug, the tension of some muscles increases to a degree corresponding to the amount of the injected drugs. But the degree of tension of the muscle at the time of injection determines what the change of the tension will be. If the tension at the time of injection is below a certain level (below average tension), the effect will be greater than if it were in the average state of tension. If the tension is above average, the effect of the same amount of injection will be less; while in a very high state of tension, the effect will be reversed, and there will no longer be an increase of tension but a decrease. To give an example, the relaxed stomach contracts under adrenalin, the contracted stomach relaxes. We know of many similar examples, particularly in the field of the vegetative nervous system. Thus we have evidence of the fact that the *same stimulus has a different effect when it touches the organism during various states of excitation.* The effect is to be understood only if we consider it not merely in terms of the working of the stimulus, but also in terms of the tendency of the organism to return to the average state of excitation. If the stimulated region is in a low state of excitation, then a stimulus which usually has the effect of producing a particular degree of excitation may produce a stronger reaction because it will be working in the same direction as the tendency to return to the average state. If the stimulated region is in a state of excitation close to the average state, the same stimulus will act less forcibly. If it is in a state of excitation above average, then the stimulus leads to a reaction of opposite character; that is, it diminishes the excitation, because the tendency to return to the average state is effective in addition to the working of the stimulus; if the stimulus were operating alone, it would result in the expected increase of excitation. This tendency is the basis for the maintenance of the threshold in spite of the fact that stimulation always changes the organism and its sensitivity to further stimulation. In normal life, after a period of time, excitation which has been changed by a stimulus becomes equalized, returns to its normal state of excitation. Thus when a new stimulus reaches the organism it is again in a state in which the threshold to stimuli is constant. This equalization process guarantees the equality of the threshold, and with that the stability and the existence of the organism. Therefore we speak of equalization as the basic biological phenomenon. How important this equalization is for the organism may be demonstrated by the fact that, when the organism is responding in an abnormal way (having lost this average, or mean, state through abnormal conditions), it responds to a new stimulation not with the reaction generally evoked but by a return to the average state of excitation. In connection with this problem, see I. H. WILDER, "Ein unbeachtetes biologisches Gesetz, sein Bedeutung für Forschung und Praxis," *Wiener klinische Wochenschrift*, vol. II, 1939, and GOLDSTEIN, *The Organism*, pp. 73 ff., where other examples are mentioned.

8. On the problem of isolation, see GOLDSTEIN, *The Organism*, pp. 133 ff.

9. EDGAR RUBIN, *Visuell wahrgenommene Figuren* (Copenhagen, 1931). See also MOLLY HARROWER, "Some Factors Deter-

mining Figure-Ground Articulation," *British Journal of Psychology*, vol. XXII, 1936, and "Changes in Figure-Ground Perception in Patients with Cortical Lesions," *British Journal of Psychology*, vol. XXX, 1939.

10. ERNST CASSIRER, *Philosophie der symbolischen Formen* (Berlin, 1929), III, 26.

11. See GOLDSTEIN, *The Organism*, p. 98.

12. See WILLIAM JAMES, *The Will to Believe, and Other Essays* (New York, 1897).

13. R. B. PERRY, *In the Spirit of William James* (New Haven, 1938).

CHAPTER II

1. On the problem of "archaic thinking," see ALFRED STORCH, "The Primitive Archaic Forms of Inner Experiences and Thought in Schizophrenia," *Journal of Nervous and Mental Disease*, Monograph Series, no. 36, 1924.

2. There is an immense amount of medical literature on the subject. A few books and articles particularly suited to non-medical readers are: HENRY HEAD, *Aphasia and Kindred Disorders of Speech* (New York, 1926); KURT GOLDSTEIN and ADHEMAR GELB, *Psychologische Analysen hirnpathologischer Fälle* (Leipsig, 1920), partially translated in W. D. ELLIS, *Source Book of Gestalt Psychology* (New York, 1938), §§ 26–30; KURT GOLDSTEIN, "The Problem of the Meaning of Words," *Journal of Psychology*, vol. II, 1936, and "The Modifications of Behavior Consequent to Cerebral Lesions," *Psychiatric Quarterly*, vol. X, 1936; THEODORE WEISENBURG and KATHARINE McBRIDE, *Aphasia* (New York, 1935); KARL ZUCKER, "An Analysis of Disturbed Function in Aphasia," *Brain*, vol. LVII, 1934; KURT GOLDSTEIN, *Die Behandlung, Fürsorge und Begutachtung der Hirnverletzten* (Leipsig, 1918).

3. For the problem of localization see CARL MONAKOW and RICHARD MOURGUE, *Biologische Einführung in das Studium der Neurologie* (Stuttgart, 1930); KURT GOLDSTEIN, "Lokalisation in der Grosshirnrinde," *Handbuch der normalen und pathologischen Physiologie*, vol. X, 1927, and *The Organism* (New York, 1939); K. S. LASHLEY, "Functional Determinants of Cerebral Localisation," *Archives of Neurology and Psychiatry*, vol. XXXVIII, 1937.

4. Kurt Goldstein and Adhemar Gelb, *Psychologische Analysen hirnpathologischer Fälle* (Leipsig, 1920); Kurt Goldstein, "The Significance of the Frontal Lobes for Mental Performances," *Journal of Neurology and Psychopathology*, vol. XVII, 1936.

5. See Kurt Goldstein and S. E. Katz, "The Psychopathology of Pick's Disease," *Archives of Neurology and Psychiatry*, vol. XXXVIII, 1937.

6. On the problem of the impairment of abstract behavior see Goldstein and Gelb, "Über Farbennamenamnesie," *Psychologische Forschung*, vol. VI, 1925; M. M. Bolles and Kurt Goldstein, "A Study of Impairment of Abstract Behavior in Schizophrenics," *Psychiatric Quarterly*, vol. XII, 1938; A. B. Nadel, "A Qualitative Analysis of Behavior Following Cerebral Lesions," *Archives of Psychology*, vol. 224, 1938; Eugenia Hanfmann and Jacob Kasanin, "A Method for the Study of Concept Formation," *Journal of Psychology*, vol. III, 1937, and *Journal of Psychiatry*, vol. XCV, 1938; Eugenia Hanfmann, "Analysis of the Thinking Disorder in a Case of Schizophrenia," *Archives of Neurology and Psychiatry*, vol. XLI, 1939; M. M. Bolles, "The Basis of Pertinence," *Archives of Psychology*, vol. 212, 1937.

7. On the problem of art and mental disease see especially Hans Prinzhorn, *Die Bildnerei der Geisteskranken* (Berlin, 1922).

8. For the block test see Goldstein and Bolles, "A Study of Impairment of Abstract Behavior in Schizophrenics," *Psychiatric Quarterly*, vol. XII, 1938; Nadel, "A Qualitative Analysis of Behavior Following Cerebral Lesions," *Archives of Psychology*, vol. 224, 1938; Kurt Goldstein and Martin Scheerer, "Abstract and Concrete Behavior: An Experimental Study with Special Tests" (in preparation).

CHAPTER III

1. See Henry Head, *Aphasia and Kindred Disorders of Speech* (New York, 1926); Theodore Weisenburg and Katharine McBride, *Aphasia* (New York, 1935); Kurt Goldstein, *Über Aphasie* (Zurich, 1927).

2. See Kurt Goldstein and Adhemar Gelb, *Psychologische Analysen hirnpathologischer Fälle* (Leipsig, 1920); Kurt Gold-

STEIN, "The Problem of the Meaning of Words Based upon Observation of Aphasic Patients," *Journal of Psychology*, vol. II, 1936; ERNST CASSIRER, *Philosophie der symbolischen Formen*, vol. II (Berlin, 1928).

3. EVA ROTHMANN, "Untersuchung eines Falles von umschriebener Hirnschädigung mit Störungen auf verschiedenen Leistungsgebieten," *Schweizer Archiv für Neurologie und Psychiatrie*, vol. XXXIII, 1933.

CHAPTER IV

1. See KURT GOLDSTEIN, "The Significance of the Frontal Lobes for Mental Performances," *Journal of Neurology and Psychopathology*, vol. XVII, 1936, and WILHELM SIEKMANN, "Psychologische Analyse eines falles Rat," *Psychologische Forschung*, vol. XVI, 1932.

2. See GOLDSTEIN, *The Organism*, pp. 35 ff.

3. See HEINRICH KLUEVER, *Behavior Mechanisms in Monkeys* (Chicago, 1933).

4. See KURT KOFFKA's distinction between geographical and behavioral milieu: KOFFKA, *Principles of Gestalt Psychology* (New York, 1935).

5. See SIGMUND FREUD, *Hemmung, Symptom, und Angst* (Leipsig, 1926); WILLIAM STERN, *Psychology of Early Childhood* (New York, 1931); KURT GOLDSTEIN, "Zum Problem der Angst," *Allgemeine Zeitschrift für Psychotherapie*, vol. II, 1927, and *The Organism*, pp. 291 ff.; SØREN KIERKEGAARD, *Der Begriff der Angst* (Jena, 1923); KAREN HORNEY, *New Ways in Psychoanalysis* (New York, 1939).

CHAPTER V

1. For this theory see G. W. ALLPORT, *Personality: A Psychological Interpretation* (New York, 1937).

2. See C. J. HERRICK, *The Brains of Rats and Men* (Chicago, 1926); G. E. COGHILL, *Anatomy and the Problem of Behavior* (New York, 1929); K. S. LASHLEY, *Brain Mechanisms and Intelligence* (Chicago, 1929); ALBRECHT BETHE, "Plastizität und Centrenlehre," *Handbuch der normalen und pathologischen Physi-*

ologie, vol. XV, 1930; KURT GOLDSTEIN, "Über die Plastizität des Organismus," *Handbuch der normalen und pathologischen Physiologie,* vol. XV, 1930.

3. On the theory of reflexes, see JOHN DEWEY, "The Reflex Arc Concept in Psychology," *Psychological Review,* vol. III, 1896. KURT GOLDSTEIN, *The Organism* (New York, 1939), lists the pertinent literature.

4. PAUL HOFFMANN and ERNST KRETSCHMER, *Untersuchungen über Eigenreflexe* (Berlin, 1922).

5. HANS DRIESCH, *Philosophie des Organischen* (Leipsig, 1928).

6. See JOHN DEWEY, "The Reflex Arc Concept in Psychology," *Psychological Review,* vol. III, 1896; R. S. WOODWORTH, *Dynamic Psychology* (New York, 1926); ALLPORT, *Personality, A Psychological Interpretation* (New York, 1937); HEINRICH KLUEVER, *Behavior Mechanisms in Monkeys* (Chicago, 1933); KURT KOFFKA, *Principles of Gestalt Psychology* (New York, 1935); I. R. KANTOR, *A Survey of the Science of Psychology* (Bloomington, Ind., 1933); R. H. WHEELER, *The Science of Psychology* (New York, 1940); I. W. CARTER, JR., "An Experimental Study of Psychological Stimulus Response," *Psychological Record,* vol. II, 1938.

7. E. C. TOLMAN, in *Psychological Review,* vol. XLV, 1938.

8. C. L. HULL, "Mind, Mechanism, and Adaptive Behavior," *Psychological Review,* vol. XLIV, 1937.

9. L. W. GELLERMANN, "Form Discrimination in Chimpanzees," *Journal of Genetic Psychology,* vol. XLII, 1933; K. F. MUENZINGER, "Motivation in Learning," *Journal of Comparative Psychology,* vols. XVII, XX, XXI, 1934–37 (seven papers).

10. "An Experimental Study of Psychological Stimulus Response," *Psychological Record,* vol. II, 1938.

11. See I. P. PAVLOV, *Conditioned Reflexes* (Oxford, 1927). An enormous amount of literature has been accumulated on conditioned reflexes; for a bibliography see R. S. WOODWORTH, *Experimental Psychology* (New York, 1938). Critical work concerning this concept will be found in the article by KARL ZENER, "The Significance of Behavior Accompanying Conditioned Salivary Secretion for Theories of the Conditioned Response," *American Journal of Psychology,* vol. L, 1937, and in H. S. LIDDELL, "The Conditioned Reflex," in *Comparative Reflexology* (New York, 1934).

12. See, on the subject, KURT KOFFKA, *The Growth of the Mind* (London, 1928), and GOLDSTEIN, *The Organism*, chap. IX, pp. 157 ff.

13. In addition to the references in note 12, see WILLIAM McDOUGALL, *Introduction to Social Psychology* (London, 1908) and *Psychoanalysis and Social Psychology* (London, 1935).

14. WOODWORTH, *Dynamic Psychology* (New York, 1926).

15. ALLPORT, *Personality, A Psychological Interpretation.*

CHAPTER VI

1. See WILLIAM STERN, *Psychology of Early Childhood* (New York, 1930); KURT KOFFKA, *The Growth of the Mind* (New York, 1925); G. E. COGHILL, *Anatomy and the Problem of Behavior* (New York, 1929); MAX MINKOWSKI, "Sur les mouvements," etc., *Revue neurologique*, vol. XXXVII, 1921, pp. 1105–18, 1235–50, and "Zur Entwicklungsgeschichte," etc., *Archiv für Neurologie und Psychiatrie*, vol. XIII, 1923, p. 475; LEONARD CARMICHAEL, "The Development of Behavior," *Psychological Review*, vol. XXXIII, 1926; N. L. MUNN, *Psychological Development* (New York, 1938); KURT GOLDSTEIN, *The Organism* (New York, 1939), chap. IX.

2. See SIGMUND FREUD, *Collected Papers* (London, 1934).

3. KAREN HORNEY, *New Ways in Psychoanalysis* (New York, 1939). See also GOLDSTEIN, *The Organism*, chap. IX, and MARTIN SCHEERER, *Die Lehre von der Gestalt* (Berlin, 1931).

CHAPTER VII

1. On preferred behavior, see KURT GOLDSTEIN, "Zum Problem der Tendenz zum ausgezeichneten Verhalten," *Deutsche Zeitschrift für Nervenheilkunde*, vol. CVII, 1929.

2. See WERTHEIMER, "Untersuchungen zur Lehre von der Gestalt," *Zeitschrift für Psychologie*, vol. LXI, 1912 (translated in W. D. ELLIS, *Source Book of Gestalt Psychology*, New York, 1938, lectures II, V).

3. See ERNST KRETSCHMER, *Körperbau und Charakter* (Berlin, 1918).

4. See FRANZ BOAS, *The Mind of Primitive Men* (New York, 1911), and OTTO KLINEBERG, *Race Differences* (New York, 1935).

CHAPTER VIII

1. WILLIAM McDOUGALL, *Introduction to Social Psychology* (London, 1908).

2. See JOHN DOLLARD and others, *Frustration and Aggression* (New Haven, 1939).

3. See ELLIS FREEMAN, *Social Psychology* (New York, 1936).

4. ERNST CASSIRER, *Philosophie der symbolischen Formen* (Berlin, 1929).

5. On customs see RUTH BENEDICT, *Patterns of Culture* (New York, 1934), and MARGARET MEAD, *Sex and Temperament in Three Primitive Societies* (New York, 1935).

CHAPTER IX

1. ÉTIENNE GILSON, *The Unity of Philosophical Experience* (New York, 1937).

2. HORKHEIMER, MAX, "Montaigne und die Function der Skepsis," *Deutsche Zeitschrift für Sozialforschung*, vol. VII, 1938, pp. 1 ff.

3. See HERBERT MARCUSE, "Zur Kritik des Hedonismus," *Deutsche Zeitschrift für Sozialforschung*, vol. III, 1938, pp. 55 ff.

4. KURT GOLDSTEIN, "Bemerkungen über die Bedeutung der Biologie für Soziologie," in *Studien über Autorität und Familie* (Paris, 1936), ed. Max Horkheimer, p. 656.

5. See ROBERT ULICH, *Fundamentals of Democratic Education* (New York, 1940).

INDEX

INDEX